NUCLEAR REACTION ANALYSIS:
GRAPHS AND TABLES

NUCLEAR REACTION ANALYSIS

GRAPHS AND TABLES

J. B. MARION
F. C. YOUNG

Department of Physics and Astronomy
University of Maryland
College Park, Maryland

1968

NORTH-HOLLAND PUBLISHING COMPANY – AMSTERDAM

INTERSCIENCE PUBLISHERS, A DIVISION OF

JOHN WILEY & SONS, INC. – NEW YORK

LIBRARY OF CONGRESS CATALOG CARD NUMBER: 68–16561

PUBLISHERS:

NORTH-HOLLAND PUBLISHING CO. – AMSTERDAM

SOLE DISTRIBUTORS FOR THE U.S.A. AND CANADA:
INTERSCIENCE PUBLISHERS, A DIVISION OF

JOHN WILEY & SONS, INC. – NEW YORK

PRINTED IN THE NETHERLANDS

INTRODUCTION

This set of tables and graphs is designed for the use of experimental nuclear reaction physicists in their everyday research. In the planning and in the interpretation of nuclear reaction experiments it is almost always necessary to refer to auxiliary graphs and tables of various types. In general, these graphs and tables are scattered throughout the published and unpublished literature. This book represents an attempt to assemble the more useful graphical and tabular material in such a way as to provide a convenient collection for nuclear reaction experimentalists.

The present collection is a revision of 'Nuclear Reaction Graphs,' Part 3, Nuclear Data Tables, by J. B. Marion, published by the National Academy of Sciences – National Research Council, Washington, D.C., 1960. Only fourteen of the original drawings have been retained in this revision. Sections on neutron sources and polarization have been omitted because these topics are contained in other collections. New additions include graphs on range, energy loss, and capture-and-loss effects of heavy ions. Many of the original drawings have been replotted using more recent results; for example, the curves for range and energy loss of charged particles. The format of many of the original drawings has been changed in order to facilitate their use or to convey more information; for example, the curves of charged-particle penetrability functions. Also, many new tables have been added, for example: neutron flight times, Rutherford scattering, atomic masses, nuclear radii, sum-rule limits, wave numbers, and resonance cross sections.

In an undertaking of this type it has naturally been necessary to choose with some arbitrariness the exact type and amount of information in various categories. It is hoped that the most basic and most useful information has been included in this collection. For example, very little information is included on lithium-drifted germanium detectors because the state-of-the-art concerning these detectors is changing so rapidly that any information presented would soon be of little value. In all cases, however, sufficient references have been given to enable the user to locate any additional information that might be required.

The cooperation of many researchers in making their numerical results and graphs available for this collection is gratefully acknowledged. The authors would appreciate suggestions of additional material that might be included in future compilations. Pointing out any inaccuracies in the graphical or tabular material as well as new information which may require alterations in any portion of this collection will also be appreciated.

University of Maryland
College Park, Maryland
1 December 1967

Jerry B. Marion
Frank C. Young

CONTENTS

A. GRAPHS

A. GRAPHS

I. *Range and Energy Loss of Charged Particles in Matter*

1

Figures 1–7. Ranges of charged particles

The range of a charged particle of incident energy E_i in a material in which its rate of energy loss is dE/dx is given by

$$R(E_i) = \int_0^{E_i} \frac{dE}{dE/dx}. \tag{1.1}$$

If dE/dx is known for $0 \leq E \leq E_i$, then the range can easily be calculated. Unfortunately, stopping cross sections have not been measured for very low energies nor can they be calculated with reliability at present. Therefore, computed range–energy relations are subject to considerable uncertainty at low energies. On the other hand, range *differences* from, say, 1 MeV to E_i can be calculated with confidence. The following curves give such range differences, i.e.,

$$R_{\text{diff}}(E_i) = \int_{1\,\text{MeV}}^{E_i} \frac{dE}{dE/dx}. \tag{1.2}$$

The *total* range is given by $R_{\text{diff}}(E_i) + R(1\,\text{MeV})$. The table below lists some estimates of $R(1\,\text{MeV})$ for the materials considered here. As better estimates (or actual measurements) become available, this table can be corrected. $R(1\,\text{MeV})$ for C, Al, Si, Fe, Ge, and Pb were taken from the range table of Williamson et al.[1] The estimates of $R(1\,\text{MeV})$ for sodium iodide and the calculations on which the following curves are based were kindly provided by H. Bichsel.[2]

Approximate ranges for 1 MeV

Fig. no.	Material		Particle				
			p	d	t	He^3	He^4
1	C	(mg/cm^2)	2.7	1.9	1.7	0.55	0.59
2	Al	(mm)	0.0146	0.011	0.010	0.0035	0.0037
3	Si	(mm)	0.0170	0.013	0.012	0.0041	0.0043
4	Fe	(mm)	0.0075	0.0061	0.0057	0.0019	0.0020
5	Ge	(mm)	0.0130	0.0108	0.0100	0.0033	0.0034
6	Pb	(mm)	0.0116	0.0095	0.0087	0.0027	0.0028
7	NaI	(mm)	0.0218	0.014	0.011	0.0029	0.0025

All of the range differences (except for carbon) are given in mm. The density of carbon, however, depends on its manufacture and it is recommended that the density be measured for the sample used before converting the range differences in mg/cm^2 to range differences in mm.

The tables of Williamson et al.[1], Barkas and Berger[3], and Skyrme[4] are also useful; deviations from the values shown here are generally small.

The following equations[5] are frequently useful for obtaining ranges for particles in terms of proton ranges:

$$R_d(E) = 2R_p(\tfrac{1}{2}E); \qquad R_t(E) = 3R_p(\tfrac{1}{3}E) \tag{1.3}$$

$$R_\alpha(E) \approx R_p(\tfrac{1}{4}E) + 0.25\,\text{mg/cm}^2; \qquad R_{\text{He}^3}(E) = \tfrac{3}{4}R_\alpha(\tfrac{4}{3}E) \tag{1.4}$$

where the subscripts p, d, t, α, and He^3 refer to protons, deuterons, tritons, α-particles, and He^3 ions, respectively. Of course, when range *differences* are considered, the approximate additive factor for helium ion ranges does not contribute.

[1] C. F. Williamson, J.-P. Boujot, and J. Picard, Tables of Range and Stopping Power of Chemical Elements for Charged Particles of Energy 0.05 to 500 MeV, Saclay Report CEA-R 3042, unpublished (1966). This set of tables supersedes an earlier publication (CEA-2189, 1962) which is unreliable, especially at low energies, due to a poor approximation.

[2] H. Bichsel, unpublished calculations performed at the University of Southern California Computer Science Laboratory; Professor Bichsel's cooperation is gratefully acknowledged.

[3] W. H. Barkas and M. J. Berger, in *Studies in Penetration of Charged Particles in Matter*, Nuclear Science Series, Report No. 39, NAS-NRC Publication 1133 (1964).

[4] D. J. Skyrme, Nuclear Instr. and Meth. *57* (1967) 61.

[5] See, for example, R. D. Evans, *The Atomic Nucleus* (McGraw-Hill, New York, 1955) p. 647 ff.

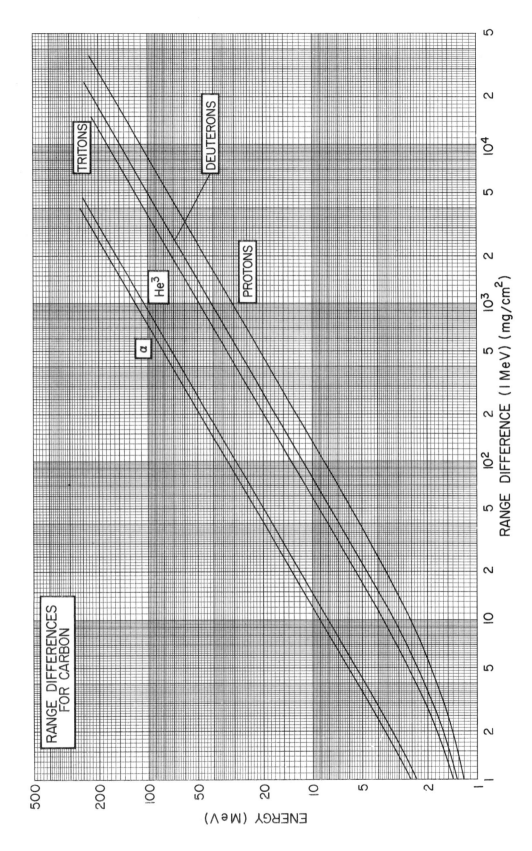

RANGE DIFFERENCES FOR CARBON

3

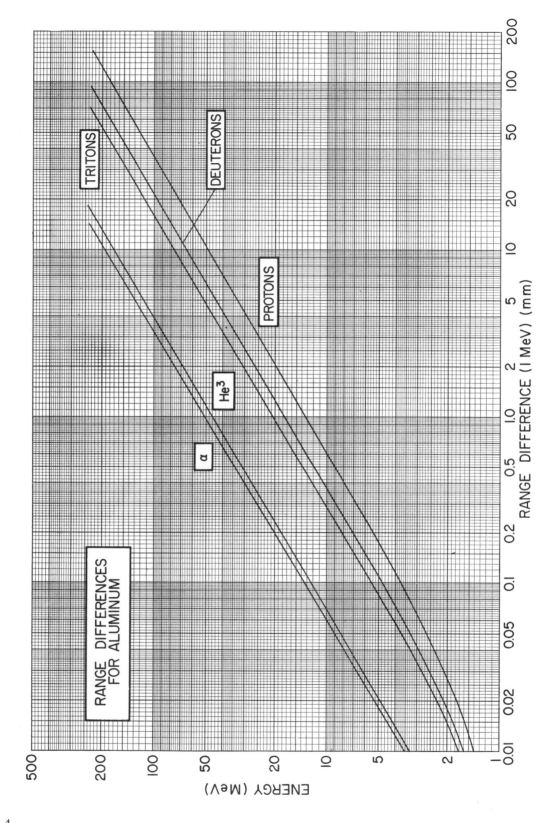

RANGE DIFFERENCES FOR ALUMINUM

TRITONS

DEUTERONS

PROTONS

He³

α

RANGE DIFFERENCE (1 MeV) (mm)

ENERGY (MeV)

4

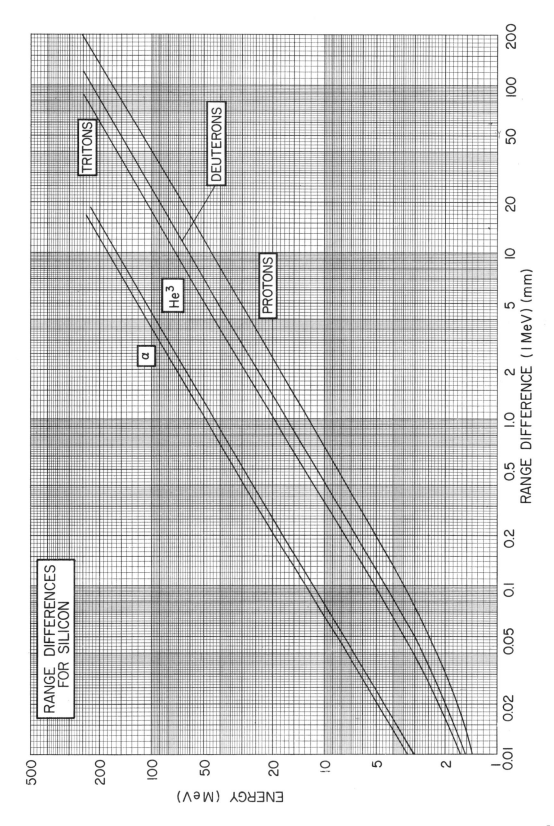

RANGE DIFFERENCES FOR SILICON

TRITONS

DEUTERONS

He³

α

PROTONS

RANGE DIFFERENCE (1 MeV) (mm)

ENERGY (MeV)

5

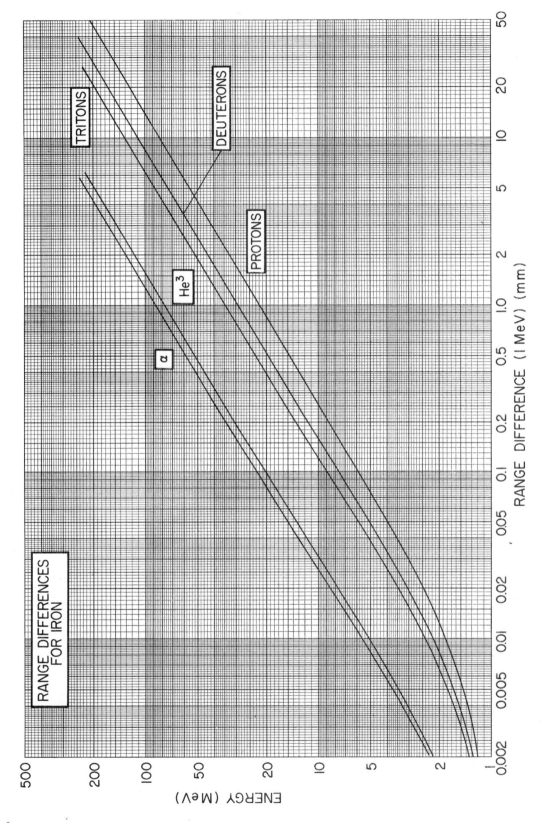

RANGE DIFFERENCES FOR IRON

TRITONS

DEUTERONS

PROTONS

He³

α

RANGE DIFFERENCE (1 MeV) (mm)

ENERGY (MeV)

6

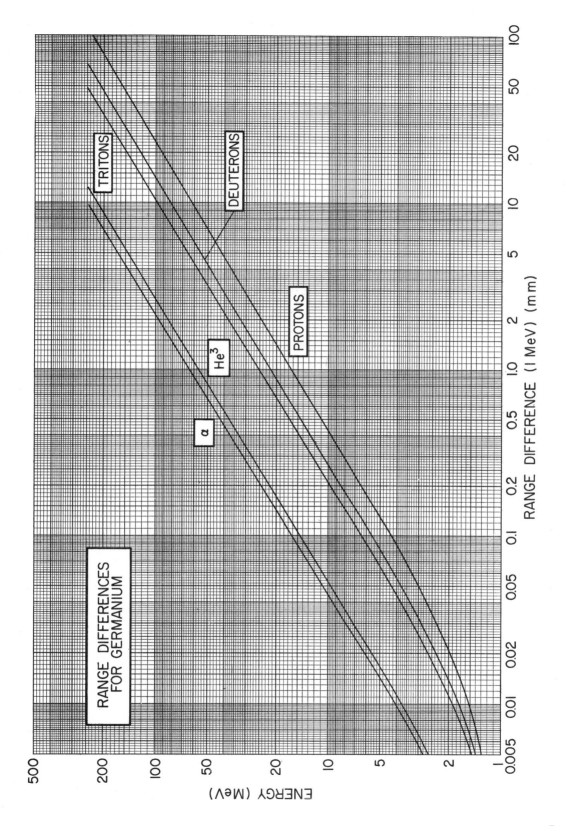

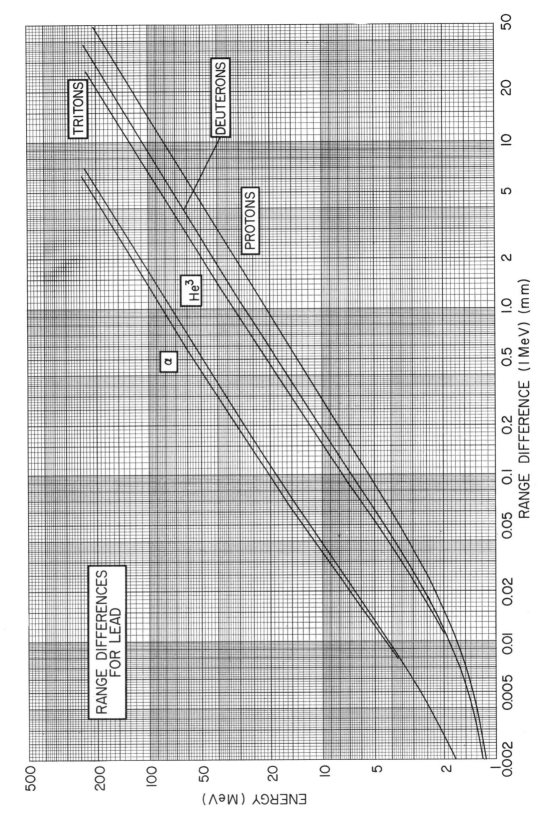

RANGE DIFFERENCES FOR LEAD

8

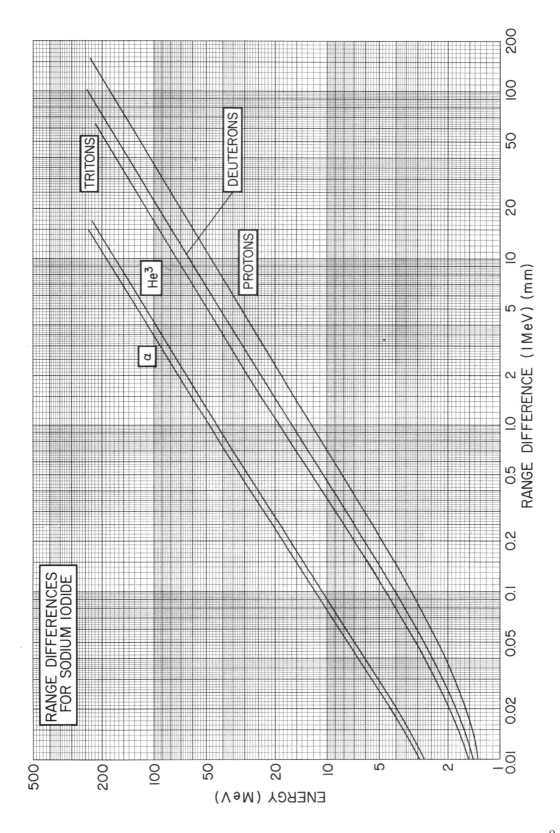

RANGE DIFFERENCES FOR SODIUM IODIDE

TRITONS

DEUTERONS

PROTONS

He³

α

RANGE DIFFERENCE (1MeV) (mm)

ENERGY (MeV)

9

Figure 8. Electron ranges in aluminum and silicon

The graph opposite gives the range of monoenergetic electrons in aluminum and silicon as a function of electron energy. Since the range (expressed in mg/cm^2) varies only slightly with the atomic number Z of the medium, this curve is approximately correct for any stopping material. Silicon is commonly used in charged particle detectors, and therefore the range of electrons in silicon as well as in aluminum is shown. This range (expressed in microns) was calculated by assuming that the range in silicon and aluminum is the same when expressed in mg/cm^2.

Katz and Penfold[1] have proposed the following empirical relationship for electron ranges:

$$R(\text{mg/cm}^2) = 412[E(\text{MeV})]^n, \qquad 0.01 < E \lesssim 3 \text{ MeV} \tag{8.1}$$

where

$$n = 1.265 - 0.0954 \ln E(\text{MeV}) \tag{8.2}$$

$$R(\text{mg/cm}^2) = 530E(\text{MeV}) - 106, \qquad 3 \lesssim E \lesssim 20 \text{ MeV} . \tag{8.3}$$

This graph is based on these relationships.

Useful tables of electron ranges in various materials have been given by Berger and Seltzer[2] and by Nelms.[3]

[1] L. Katz and A. S. Penfold, Revs. Modern Phys. *24* (1952) 28.

[2] M. J. Berger and S. M. Seltzer, in *Studies in Penetration of Charged Particles in Matter*, Nuclear Science Series, Report No. 39, NAS-NRC Publication 1133 (1964).

[3] A. T. Nelms, *Energy Loss and Range of Electrons and Positrons*, National Bureau of Standards Circular 577 (1956).

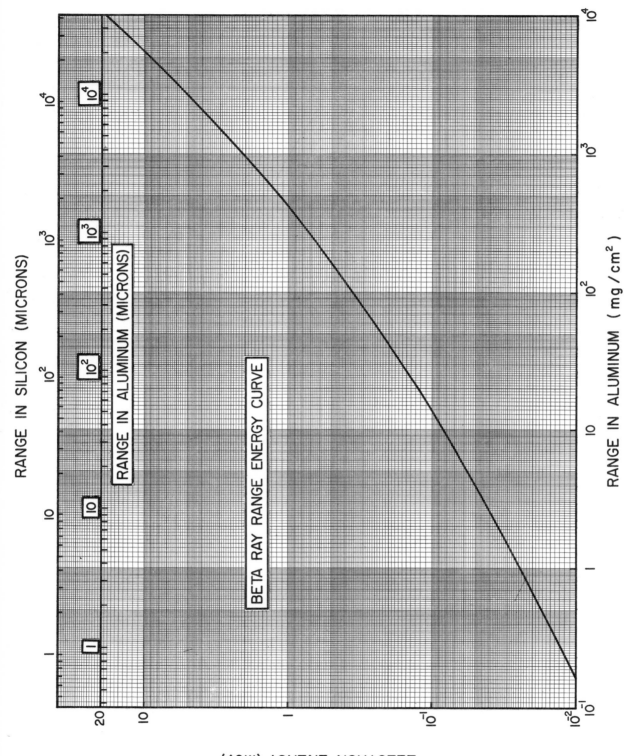

RANGE IN SILICON (MICRONS)

RANGE IN ALUMINUM (MICRONS)

BETA RAY RANGE ENERGY CURVE

RANGE IN ALUMINUM (mg / cm²)

ELECTRON ENERGY (MeV)

11

Figure 9. *Average proton stopping cross sections, ε vs. Z*

In order to facilitate the estimation of atomic stopping cross sections of elements for which no measurements are available, the accompanying graph represents average stopping cross sections as functions of Z for proton energies of 0.5, 1.0, 2.0, and 4.0 MeV. The data points, through which the average curves are drawn, are from the review article by Whaling.[1] Fluctuations from the smooth curve are real and limit the accuracy of estimating ε for elements not shown. The conversion from ε to dE/dx may be accomplished by means of the factors given in Table 3, page 137.

The values of ε for protons shown in this figure may be converted to values of ε for other charged particles by using the relationships given in eqs. (10.1) through (10.4) on page 14 which apply for ε as well as for dE/dx.

The molecular stopping cross section of a compound X_aY_b may be computed from the atomic stopping cross sections of the constituent atoms:

$$\varepsilon_{\mathrm{mol}}(X_aY_b) = a\varepsilon_{\mathrm{at}}(X) + b\varepsilon_{\mathrm{at}}(Y) . \tag{9.1}$$

[1] W. Whaling, in *Handbuch der Physik*, ed. E. Flügge, Vol. 34 (Springer-Verlag, Berlin, 1958) p. 193.

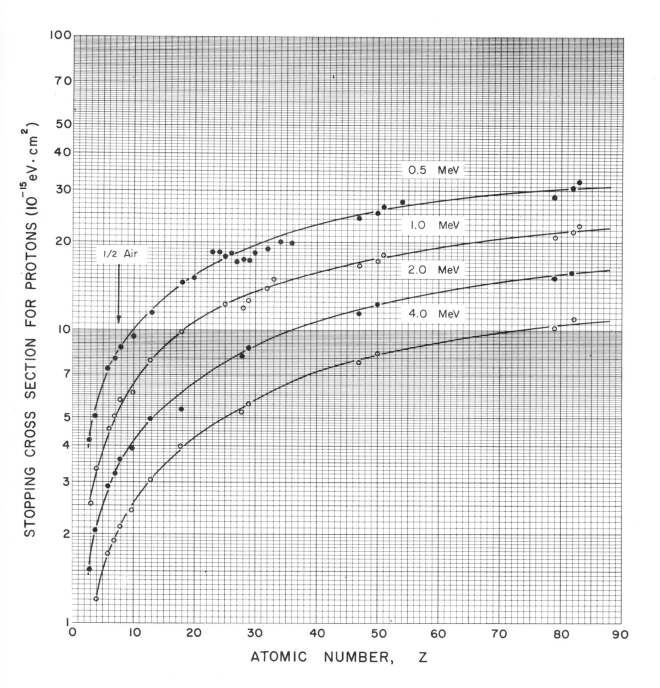

ATOMIC NUMBER, Z

Y-axis: STOPPING CROSS SECTION FOR PROTONS (10^{-15} eV·cm^2)

1/2 Air

0.5 MeV
1.0 MeV
2.0 MeV
4.0 MeV

Figures 10–14.   *Energy loss of charged particles in matter*

The following graphs give the rates of energy loss for protons in some of the materials commonly used as targets, detectors, and stopping foils. Included are the following:

Fig. no.	Material(s)	Units of dE/dx
10	C, Al, Fe, Pb	keV/(mg/cm^2)
11	Be, Cu, Ge, Au	keV/(mg/cm^2)
12	Si	keV/mm
13	H, N, O, Kr	keV/cm at NTP
14	He, Ne, Ar, Xe	keV/cm at NTP

Figure 12 shows, in addition, dE/dx (in keV/mm) for deuterons, tritons, He^3, and α-particles in silicon. These additional curves are given for convenience because silicon is a common detector material, but, in general, these curves can be obtained from the proton curves by using the following relations:

$$\left.\frac{dE}{dx}(\text{deuteron})\right|_E = \left.\frac{dE}{dx}(\text{proton})\right|_{\frac{1}{2}E} \tag{10.1}$$

$$\left.\frac{dE}{dx}(\text{triton})\right|_E = \left.\frac{dE}{dx}(\text{proton})\right|_{\frac{1}{3}E} \tag{10.2}$$

$$\left.\frac{dE}{dx}(\text{He}^3)\right|_E = 4\left.\frac{dE}{dx}(\text{proton})\right|_{\frac{1}{3}E} \tag{10.3}$$

$$\left.\frac{dE}{dx}(\alpha)\right|_E = 4\left.\frac{dE}{dx}(\text{proton})\right|_{\frac{1}{4}E}. \tag{10.4}$$

The factor 4 that appears in eqs. (10.3) and (10.4) is valid only when the equilibrium charge of the helium ion is essentially 2 (see Fig. 16). The factor to be used when the ion is not completely stripped is given in Fig. 16.

If it is desired to convert dE/dx (in keV/mg/cm^2) to the stopping cross section ε (in eV-cm^2), the relevant factors can be found in Table 3. In order to convert from keV/mm, the density of the material is needed; these can be found in Table 1.

The curves for $E \gtrsim 3$ MeV are based on the calculations of Bichsel.[1] For $E \lesssim 1$ MeV, the curves are those given by Whaling.[2] The two sets were joined smoothly in the region $1 < E < 3$ MeV. The curves for silicon are in agreement with the tables of Skyrme[3] for $E(\text{proton}) \gtrsim 3$ MeV.

[1] H. Bichsel, unpublished calculations performed at the University of Southern California Computer Science Laboratory; Professor Bichsel's cooperation is gratefully acknowledged.
[2] W. Whaling, in *Handbuch der Physik*, ed. E. Flügge, Vol. 34 (Springer-Verlag, Berlin, 1958) p. 193; and supplement by D. Demirlioglu and W. Whaling, California Institute of Technology, unpublished (1962).
[3] D. J. Skyrme, Nuclear Instr. and Meth. 57 (1967) 61.

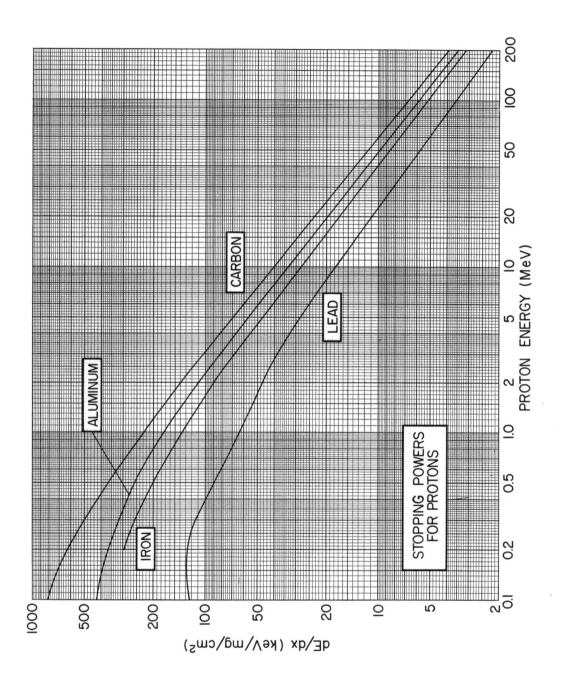

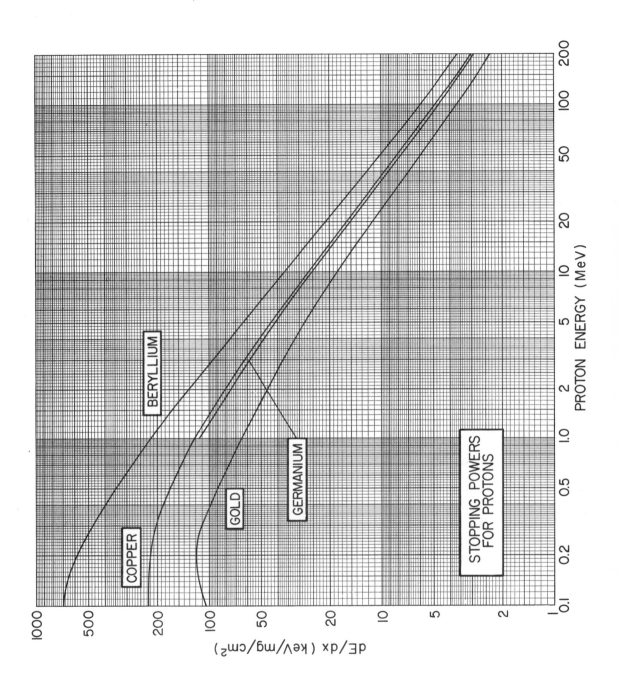

STOPPING POWERS FOR PROTONS

BERYLLIUM

COPPER

GOLD

GERMANIUM

PROTON ENERGY (MeV)

dE/dx (keV/mg/cm²)

16

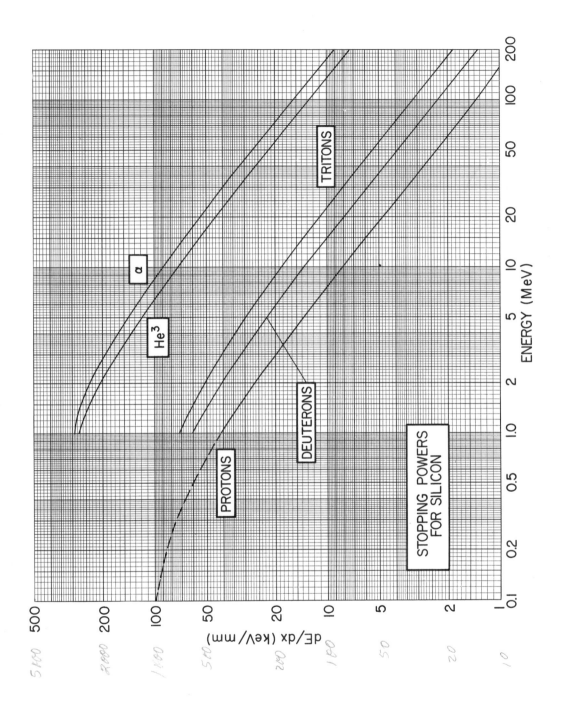

STOPPING POWERS FOR SILICON

17

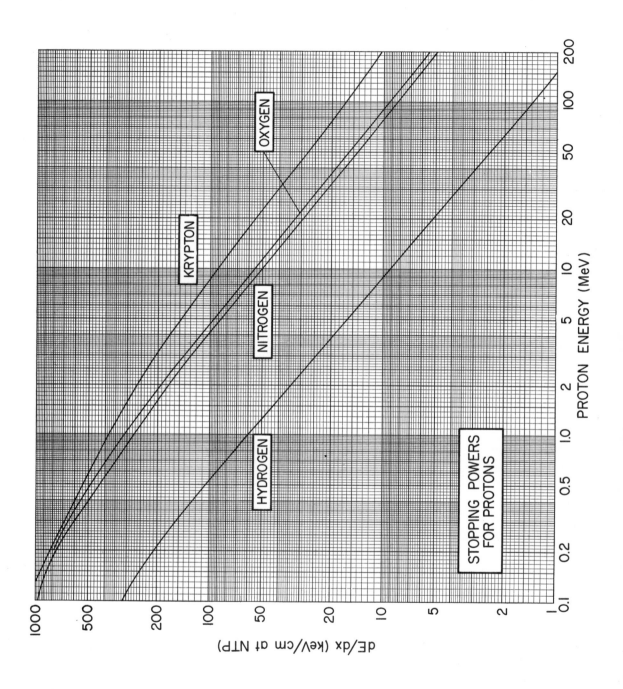

18

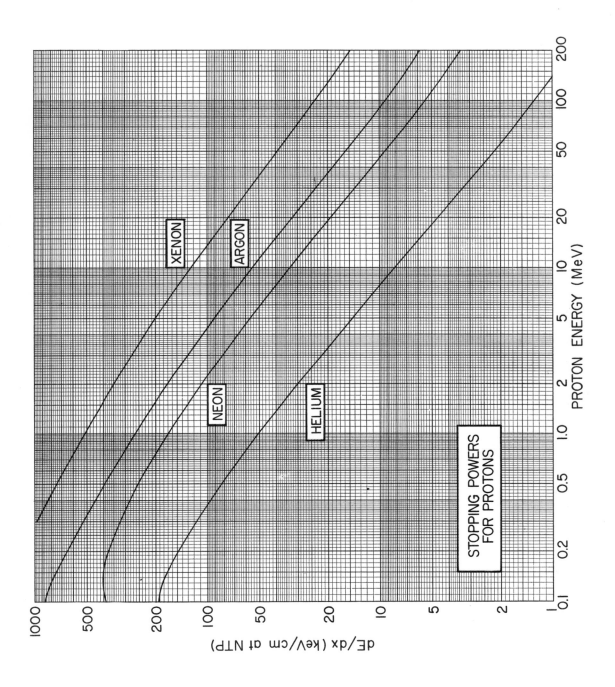

STOPPING POWERS FOR PROTONS

XENON

ARGON

NEON

HELIUM

dE/dx (keV/cm at NTP)

PROTON ENERGY (MeV)

19

Figure 15. *Specific energy loss for electrons in silicon*

The rate of energy loss of electrons in matter (in units of keV/mg/cm^2) is a slowly varying function of the atomic number Z of the material. Because of its importance in charged particle detection, silicon has been selected as the material for which to present a curve of dE/dx for electrons. Units of keV/mm have been chosen to simplify calculations for silicon detectors. The value of dE/dx for other materials with not too different Z may be obtained by multiplying the value of dE/dx from the curve by the ratio of the density of the material to the density of silicon (2.33 g/cm^3).

The values of dE/dx used in constructing the curve were taken from the calculations of Nelms.[1] Useful tables have also been given by Berger and Seltzer.[2]

[1] A. T. Nelms, Energy Loss and Range of Electrons and Positrons, National Bureau of Standards Circular 577 (1956).

[2] M. J. Berger and S. M. Seltzer, in *Studies in Penetration of Charged Particles in Matter*, Nuclear Science Series Report No. 39, NAS-NRC Publication 1133 (1964).

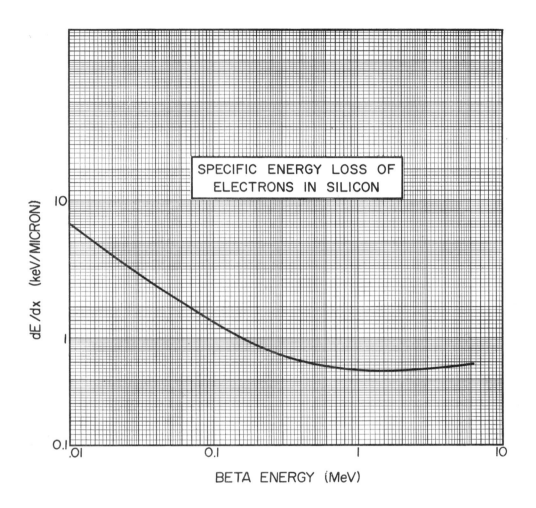

Figure 16.   Ratio of α-particle stopping cross sections to proton stopping cross sections

Due to the capture and loss of orbital electrons by helium ions traversing matter, a certain equilibrium charge results for the helium ions and this charge depends on the ion velocity. Therefore, the computation of the energy loss by helium ions from data obtained for protons is complicated in the low-energy region. If the equilibrium helium ion charge at energy E is $\bar{Z}$, then:

$$\varepsilon(\alpha\text{-particle})|_E = \bar{Z}^2 \varepsilon(\text{proton})|_{\frac{1}{4}E} \tag{16.1}$$

$$\varepsilon(\text{He}^3\,\text{particle})|_E = \bar{Z}^2 \varepsilon(\text{proton})|_{\frac{1}{3}E}. \tag{16.2}$$

Values of $\bar{Z}^2$ for α-particles are given in the accompanying graph, constructed from the tabulations of Whaling.[1]

If the curve is to be used for He^3 ions, the value must be read for the energy which yields the same *velocity* for the He^3 ion as for the α-particle. That is, the value of $\bar{Z}^2$ for He^3 ions at an energy E_{He^3} is the same as that for α-particles at an energy $E_\alpha = \frac{4}{3}E_{\text{He}^3}$.

Note that if 'dE/dx' is substituted for 'ε' throughout in the above equations, the relationships remain valid.

---

[1] W. Whaling, in *Handbuch der Physik*, ed. E. Flügge, Vol. 34 (Springer-Verlag, Berlin, 1958) p. 193.

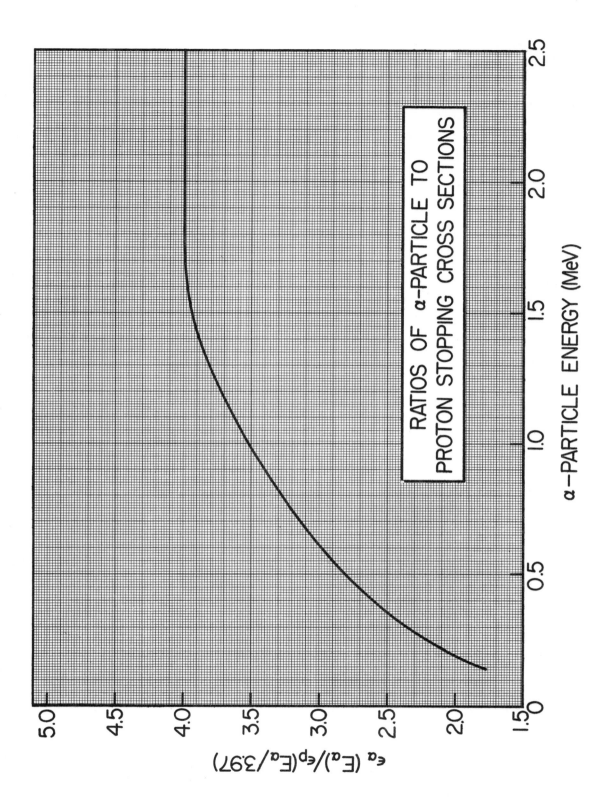

RATIOS OF α-PARTICLE TO
PROTON STOPPING CROSS SECTIONS

α-PARTICLE ENERGY (MeV)

$\epsilon_\alpha (E_\alpha)/\epsilon_p (E_\alpha/3.97)$

23

Figure 17. *Ranges of heavy ions in aluminum*

Both the experimental and theoretical status of our understanding of the passage of heavy ions through matter are much cruder than for hydrogen and helium ions. A survey has recently been given by Northcliffe[1] in which a semi-empirical method has been used to generate range curves for various heavy ions in aluminum for energies up to 11 MeV/amu. Some of these curves are shown in the accompanying graph; the original report[1] contains additional curves for several isotopes of each bombarding ion.

Hubbard[2] has calculated a set of curves for C^{12}, N^{14}, O^{16}, Ne^{20}, and Ar^{40} beams in Be, Al, Ni, Cu, Ag, Au, and Pb absorbers.

[1] L. C. Northcliffe and R. L. Gluckstern, Yale University report, unpublished, revised version (1962); L. C. Northcliffe, in *Studies in Penetration of Charged Particles in Matter*, Nuclear Science Series, Report No. 39, NAS-NRC Publication 1133 (1964). Also see Phys. Rev. *120* (1960) 1744.

[2] E. L. Hubbard, University of California Radiation Laboratory Report UCRL-9053, unpublished (1960).

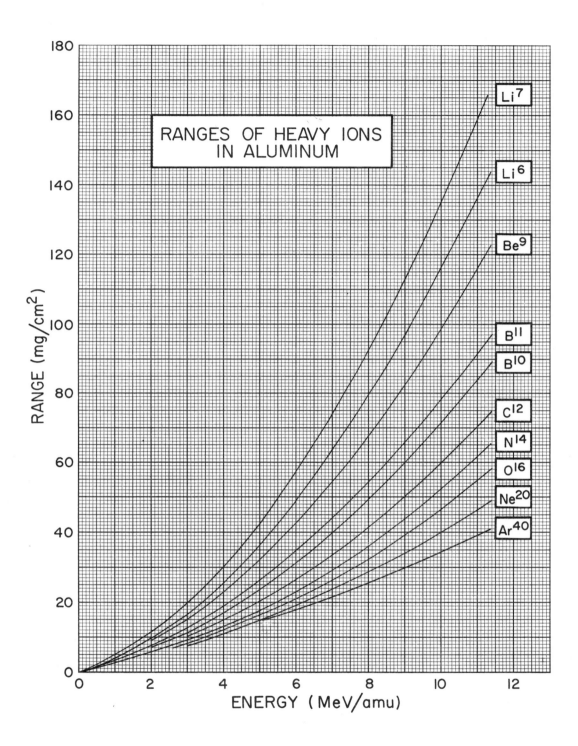

RANGES OF HEAVY IONS IN ALUMINUM

Li⁷ · Li⁶ · Be⁹ · B¹¹ · B¹⁰ · C¹² · N¹⁴ · O¹⁶ · Ne²⁰ · Ar⁴⁰

ENERGY (MeV/amu)

RANGE (mg/cm²)

25

Figures 18, 19. Energy loss of heavy ions in solids

Booth and Grant[1] have given a semi-empirical method for determining the energy loss of heavy ions in solids. The heavy-ion energy loss is expressed in terms of the energy loss of protons moving at the same velocity by:

$$\left(\frac{dE}{dx}\right)_{ion} = \frac{Z^2 \gamma_{eff}^2}{\gamma_p^2} \left(\frac{dE}{dx}\right)_p \tag{18.1}$$

where $\gamma_{eff}Z$ is the effective charge of the heavy ion (Z is the atomic number of the ion) and γ_p is the effective charge carried by the proton. Figure 18 gives a single universal curve of γ_{eff}^2 for different ions as a function of $EZ^{-\frac{4}{3}}$ where E is the ion energy per nucleon. The proton effective charge has been measured by Hall,[2] and the curve of Booth and Grant,[1] interpolating these measurements, is given in Fig. 19. The energy loss of a heavy ion can be calculated with the expression above by using the proton energy loss evaluated at the proton energy equal to the ion energy per nucleon from the curves of Whaling[3] (see Figs. 10–14) and by using the effective charges from Figs. 18 and 19.

A semi-empirical method for calculating the energy loss of heavy ions based on the calculation of an equivalent aluminum absorber thickness has been given by Poth et al.[4] This method is limited to ions with $E > Z^2/9$.

[1] W. Booth and I. S. Grant, Nuclear Phys. *63* (1965) 481; and private communication. The coefficient of the x^3 term in eq. (4) of this reference should be 1131 instead of 131.

[2] T. Hall, Phys. Rev. *79* (1950) 504.

[3] W. Whaling, in *Handbuch der Physik*, ed. E. Flügge, Vol. 34 (Springer-Verlag, Berlin, 1958) p. 193; and supplement by D. Demirlioglu and W. Whaling, California Institute of Technology, unpublished (1962).

[4] J. E. Poth, J. C. Overley and D. A. Bromley, Phys. Rev. *164* (1967) 1295.

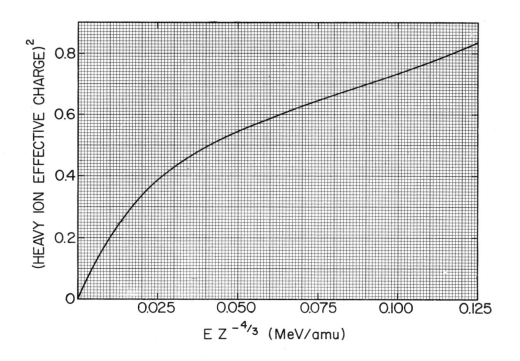

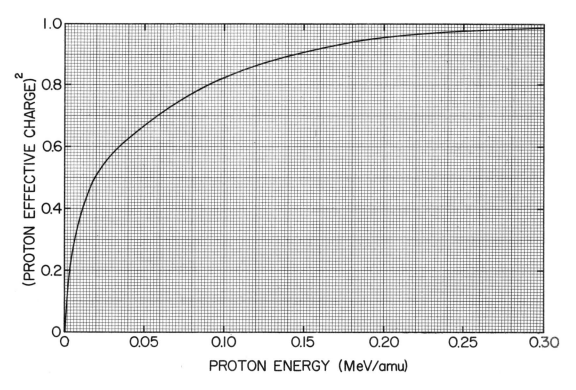

II. *Scattering, Straggling, and Capture-and-Loss Effects*

Figure 20. *Multiple scattering of charged particles*

The effects of multiple scattering are frequently important when charged particle beams are passed through thin foils. The most recent and most complete theory of multiple scattering is that given by Nigam et al.[1] Marion and Zimmerman[2] have shown that an approximate form of this theory is quite accurate for medium energy protons scattered by materials of moderate thickness. The parameters of this theory are

$$\chi_c = 0.1569 \frac{Z(Z+1)z^2 t}{A(pv)^2} \tag{20.1}$$

and B which is a root of

$$B - \ln B = b \tag{20.2}$$

where

$$b = \ln \left[2730(Z+1)Z^{\frac{1}{3}}z^2 t/A\beta^2 \right] - 0.1544 \tag{20.3}$$

in which $z(Z)$ is the atomic number of the incident particle (scatterer), A the atomic weight of the scatterer, t the thickness of the scattering foil (g/cm^2), pv the momentum–velocity product of the incident particle in MeV, $\beta = v/c$, $(pv)^2 = (E^2 + 2EMc^2)\beta^2$, and $\beta^2 = 1 - (1 + E/Mc^2)^{-2}$; and where E and Mc^2 are the incident energy and rest mass of the incident particle, respectively, in MeV.

The angular distribution is approximately Gaussian and is given by

$$F(x) \propto \exp - (x^2/x_w^2) \tag{20.4}$$

where

$$x = \theta/\chi_c B^{\frac{1}{2}} . \tag{20.5}$$

The width parameter x_w gives the angle at which the angular distribution has fallen to $1/e$ of its value at $x = 0$. The accompanying graph[2] shows the dependence of x_w on B. In order to use the graph, first compute b and χ_c from the expressions above. The value of B can be closely estimated from the table below. At the particular value of B, read the value of x_w from the graph and multiply by $\chi_c B^{\frac{1}{2}}$ to obtain $\theta_{1/e}$ (in radians). For example, consider 50-MeV protons incident on a 1 mg/cm^2 Ni foil. From eqs. (20.1) and (20.3) we find $\chi_c = 4.779 \times 10^{-4}$ and $b = 3.572$. From the table below, $B \approx 5.23$, and from the graph, $x_w = 0.867$, so that $\theta_{1/e} = 0.054°$.

The theory is valid for $4 \lesssim B \lesssim 15$, and can be used for particles other than protons by substituting the appropriate values of charge and mass.[2]

b	B	$B^{\frac{1}{2}}$	b	B	$B^{\frac{1}{2}}$
2.6	3.982	1.995	8.2	10.557	3.249
3.0	4.505	2.123	8.6	10.998	3.316
3.4	5.012	2.239	9.0	11.437	3.382
3.8	5.506	2.346	9.4	11.874	3.446
4.2	5.990	2.447	9.8	12.310	3.509
4.6	6.467	2.543	10.2	12.745	3.570
5.0	6.937	2.634	10.6	13.179	3.630
5.4	7.402	2.721	11.0	13.611	3.689
5.8	7.862	2.804	11.4	14.042	3.747
6.2	8.318	2.884	11.8	14.472	3.804
6.6	8.772	2.962	12.2	14.901	3.860
7.0	9.222	3.037	12.6	15.330	3.915
7.4	9.669	3.109	13.0	15.757	3.970
7.8	10.114	3.180	13.4	16.184	4.023

[1] B. P. Nigam, M. K. Sundaresan and T.-Y. Wu, Phys. Rev. *115* (1959) 491.
[2] J. B. Marion and B. A. Zimmerman, Nuclear Instr. and Meth. *51* (1967) 93.

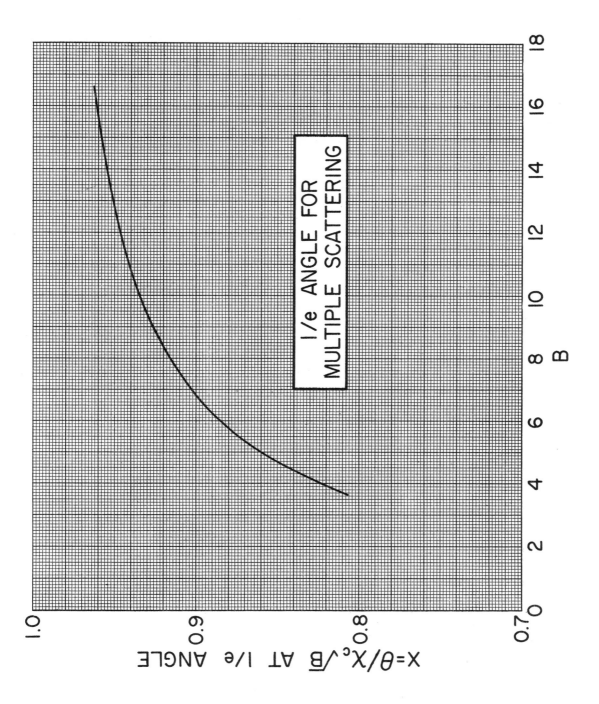

31

Figure 21. *Range straggling of protons, deuterons, and α particles*

The straggling in range of charged particles is important when absorbers are used to measure energies by the range method. Since the number of collisions of the stopping particle per unit path length is large, the Poisson distribution of ranges is well represented by a normal (Gaussian) distribution:

$$P(R)\,dR = (2\pi)^{-\frac{1}{2}}\sigma^{-1}\exp[-(R-R_0)^2/2\sigma^2]\,dR \qquad (21.1)$$

where R_0 is the mean range and 2σ is the full width of the distribution curve between the points of maximum slope. The full width at half maximum height is $2\sigma\sqrt{2\ln 2}=2.354\sigma$ and the full width at $1/e$ of the maximum height is $2\sigma\sqrt{2}=2.828\sigma$.[1]

The relationship between the mean range R_0 and the extrapolated range R_e is

$$R_0 = R_e - \sqrt{\pi/2}\,\sigma = R_e - 1.253\sigma$$

$$= R_e - \sqrt{\pi}\,\tfrac{1}{2}\alpha = R_e - 0.886\alpha \qquad (21.2)$$

where $\alpha = \sqrt{2}\,\sigma$ is the *range-straggling parameter* originally defined by Bohr.[2]

The ratio σ/R_0 is given by[3]

$$\sigma/R_0 = (102.2/Mc^2)^{\frac{1}{2}}\,f(E/Mc^2) \qquad (21.3)$$

where Mc^2 is the rest mass in MeV of the stopping particle. The function $f(E/Mc^2)$ is given in the accompanying graph[4] which is valid for particles stopping in iron. Values of σ/R_0 for other elements can be obtained from the table below.

Proton range straggling relative to Fe

Element	15 MeV	100 MeV	1 GeV
Be	0.85	0.90	0.91
Al	0.93	0.95	0.95
Cu	1.00	1.00	1.00
Ag	1.00	1.01	1.01
Pb	1.13	1.10	1.08

The range straggling of other particles can be estimated by using the approximate relation[5]

$$\sigma/R_0 = M^{-\frac{1}{2}}f(v_0, I) \qquad (21.4)$$

where $f(v_0, I)$ is a complicated, but slowly-varying function of the initial velocity and the ionization potential of the absorbing material. Therefore, for particles with the same initial velocity, the range straggling is approximately proportional to $M^{-\frac{1}{2}}$. Thus,

Deuterons:
$$\left.\frac{\sigma}{R_0}\right|_{E_d} = \frac{1}{\sqrt{2}}\left.\frac{\sigma}{R_0}(\text{protons})\right|_{E_p = 2E_d} \qquad (21.5)$$

α particles:
$$\left.\frac{\sigma}{R_0}\right|_{E_\alpha} = \left.\frac{\sigma}{2R_0}(\text{protons})\right|_{E_p = 4E_\alpha}. \qquad (21.6)$$

The approximate relation (21.4) cannot be expected to hold for very heavy ions (such as fission fragments) for which nuclear collisions greatly increase the straggling.

[1] A summary of the relations for Poisson and Gaussian distributions will be found on p. 169.
[2] N. Bohr, Phil. Mag. *30* (1915) 581.
[3] H. Bichsel, in *American Institute of Physics Handbook*, ed. D. E. Gray, 2nd edition (McGraw-Hill, New York, 1963) p. 8–37.
[4] Calculated by K. R. Symon and quoted by B. Rossi, *High Energy Particles* (Prentice-Hall, New York, 1952) p. 36.
[5] R. D. Evans, *The Atomic Nucleus* (McGraw-Hill, New York, 1955) p. 660 ff.

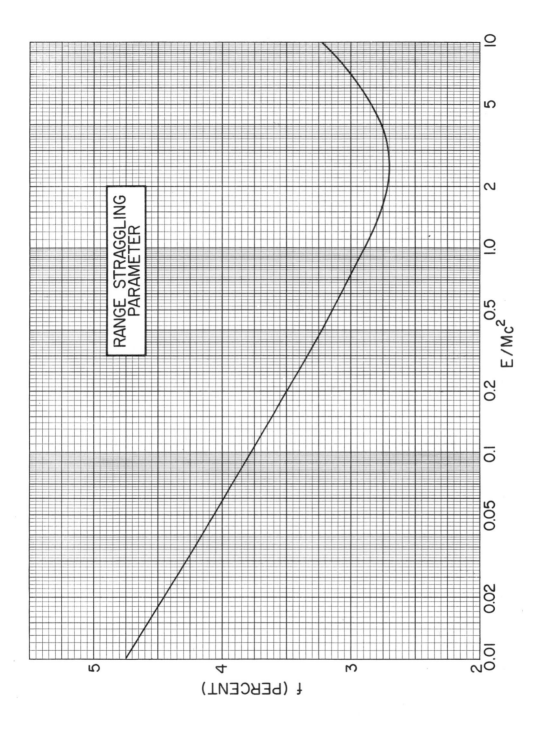

RANGE STRAGGLING PARAMETER

f (PERCENT)

E/Mc²

33

Figures 22–32. Equilibrium charge states of ions in solids

When charged particles pass through matter, they capture and lose orbital electrons until an equilibrium charge distribution is attained for the moving ions. Since there is increasing interest in studying nuclear reactions involving the emission of heavy ions with magnetic or electrostatic analyzing equipment, knowledge of the capture and loss of electrons by heavy ions is necessary. The accompanying graphs show ϕ_i, the fractions of the total beam of ions with charge i, plotted as functions of the ion velocity (v) for hydrogen, helium, lithium, beryllium, boron, carbon, nitrogen, oxygen, fluorine, and neon ions. Figure 22 relates the ion energy per nucleon to the velocity and is for use with the following ten figures of equilibrium charge states.

The charge-state fractions for helium were taken from the work of Armstrong et al.[1] The charge-state fractions for all other ions are based on calculations by Zaidins.[2] The general ideas of Dmitriev[3] were used in calculating the curves in Figs. 25–32. In this empirical method, $\phi_i(v)$ is the sum of $Z!/[i!\,(Z-i)!]$ terms, each of which is a product of i functions, $p_j(v)$, and $Z-i$ functions, $1-p_j(v)$. In these expressions, Z is the atomic number and $p_j(v)$ is the probability that the jth electron is stripped from the ion. Although this method is not entirely correct physically, it does insure that $\Sigma_i \phi_i = 1$. The curves were calculated by assuming

$$p_j(v) = 1 - \exp[-A_j(v/v_j)^{B_j}]. \tag{22.1}$$

In this expression A_j and B_j are parameters and $v_j^2 = 2I_j/m_e$ where I_j is the ionization potential for the jth electron[4] and m_e is the electron mass. The velocity v_j corresponds to the classical orbital velocity of the jth electron. A_j and B_j (the latter is arbitrarily restricted to integer or half-integer values) were determined by using a non-linear least-squares method to fit the available experimental data. Several measurements of equilibrium charge-state distributions for helium ions in solids have shown that the distributions are essentially independent of the material used.[1,5] In the following graphs this has also been assumed for other heavy ions in solids.

A general summary of charge-state equilibrium is discussed in several review articles.[5–7]

[1] J. C. Armstrong, J. V. Mullendore, W. R. Harris and J. B. Marion, Proc. Phys. Soc. (London) *86* (1965) 1283.
[2] C. Zaidins, unpublished calculations performed at the California Institute of Technology, Kellogg Radiation Laboratory; see also Appendix I, Ph. D. Thesis, C. Zaidins (1967). Dr. Zaidins' cooperation is gratefully acknowledged.
[3] I. S. Dmitriev, Soviet Phys. JETP *5* (1957) 473.
[4] Landolt-Börnstein, eds. A. Eucken and K. H. Hellwege, 6th edition, Vol. 1, section 1 (Springer-Verlag, Berlin, 1950) p. 211.
[5] S. K. Allison, Revs. Modern Phys. *30* (1958) 1137.
[6] L. C. Northcliffe, Annual Reviews of Nuclear Science *13* (1963) 67.
[7] I. S. Dmitriev and V. S. Nikolaev, Soviet Phys. JETP *20* (1965) 409.

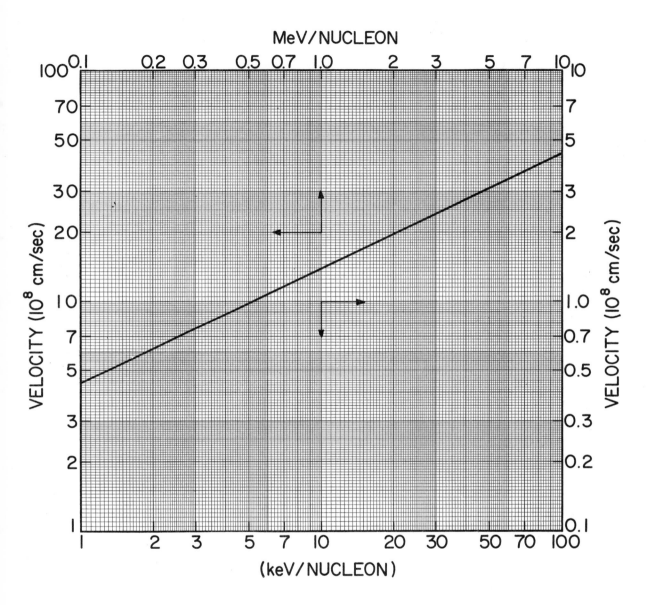

MeV/NUCLEON

(keV/NUCLEON)

VELOCITY (10^8 cm/sec)

VELOCITY (10^8 cm/sec)

35

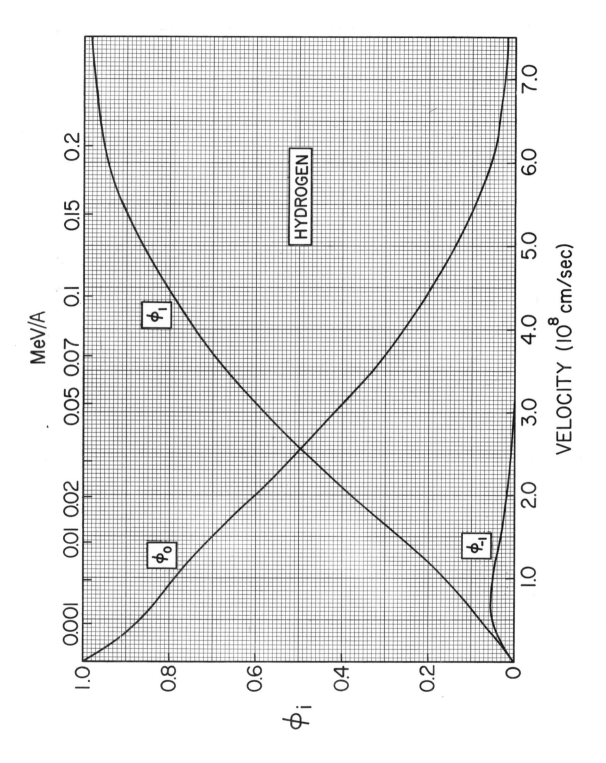

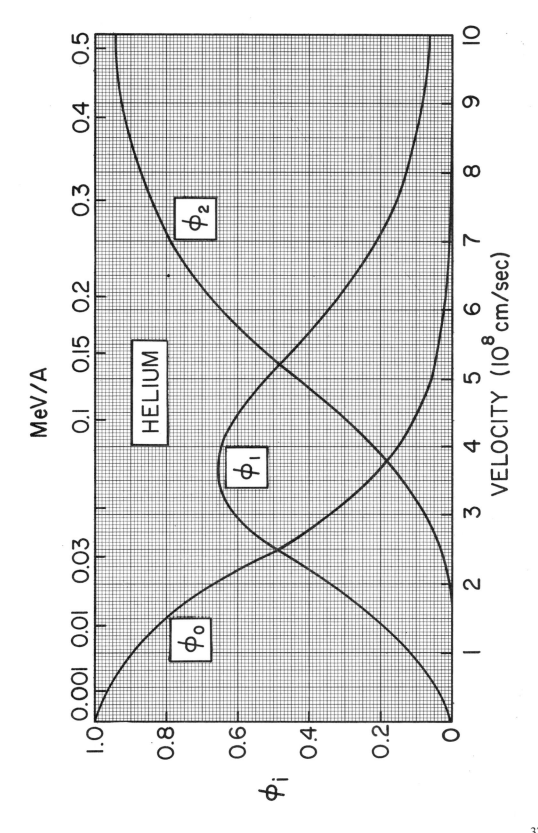

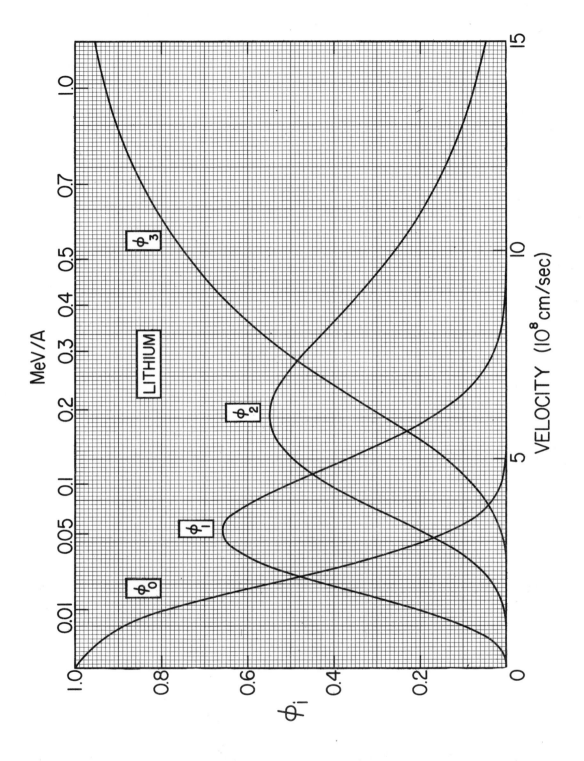

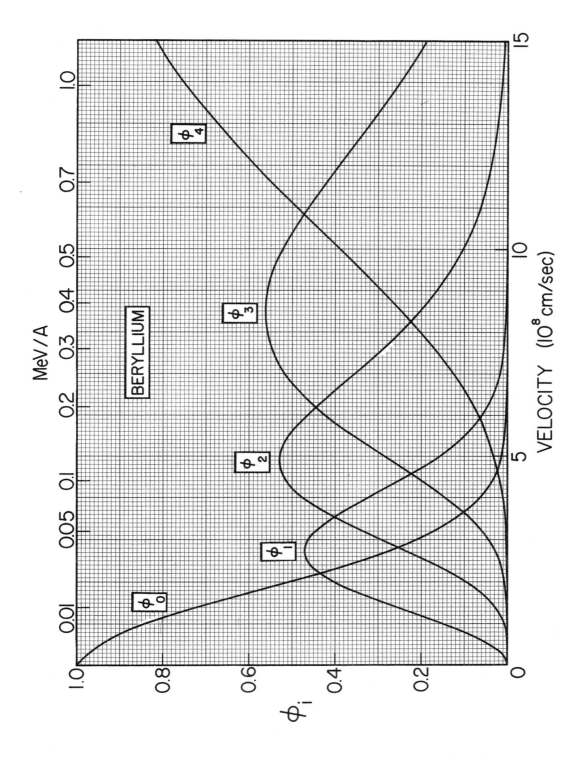

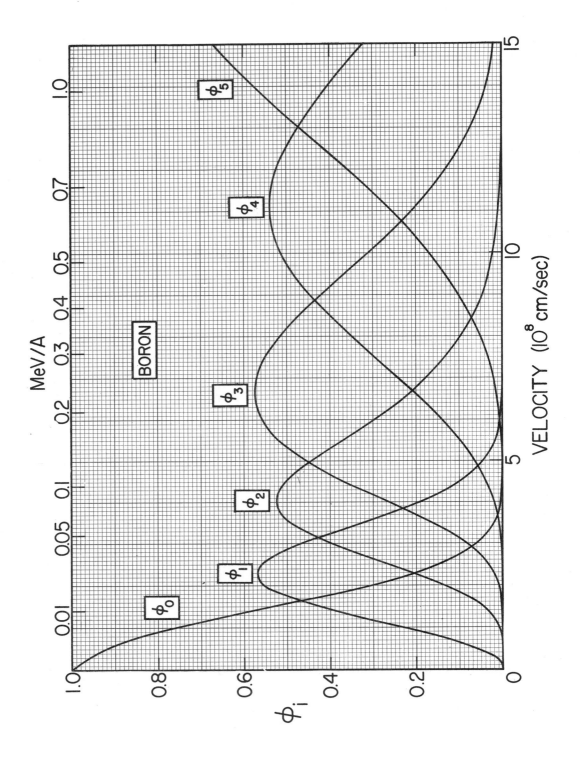

40

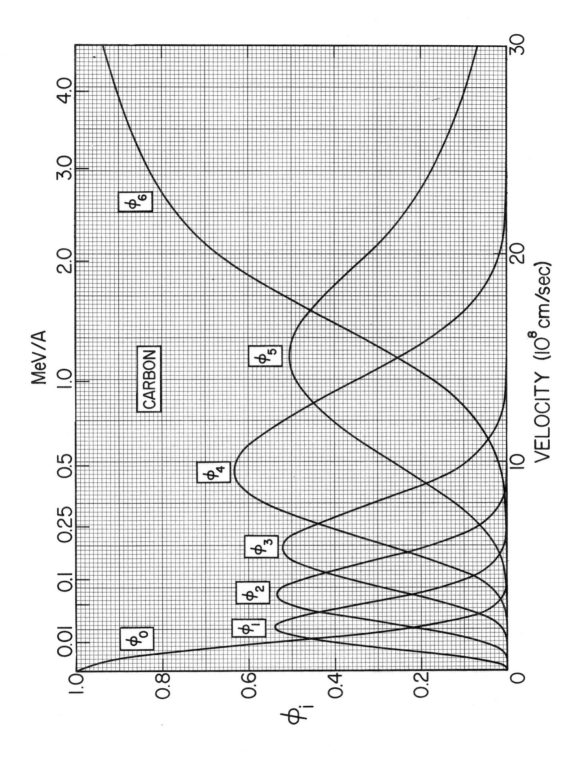

41

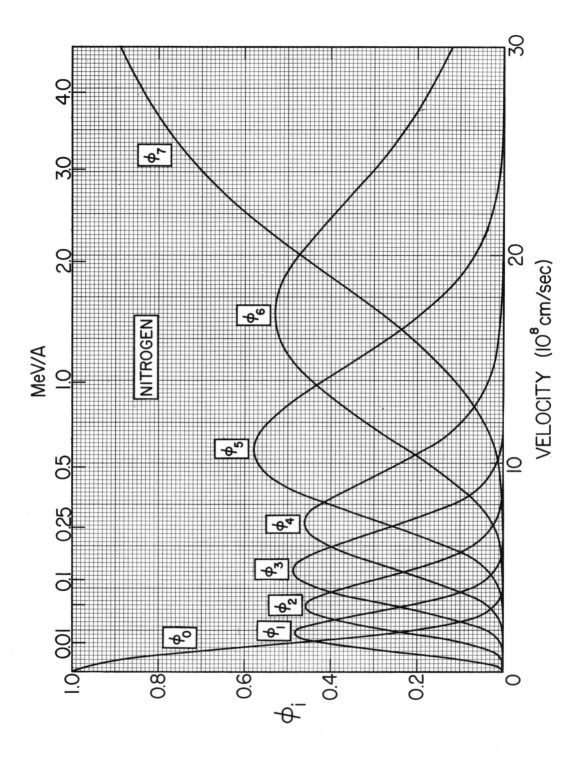

42

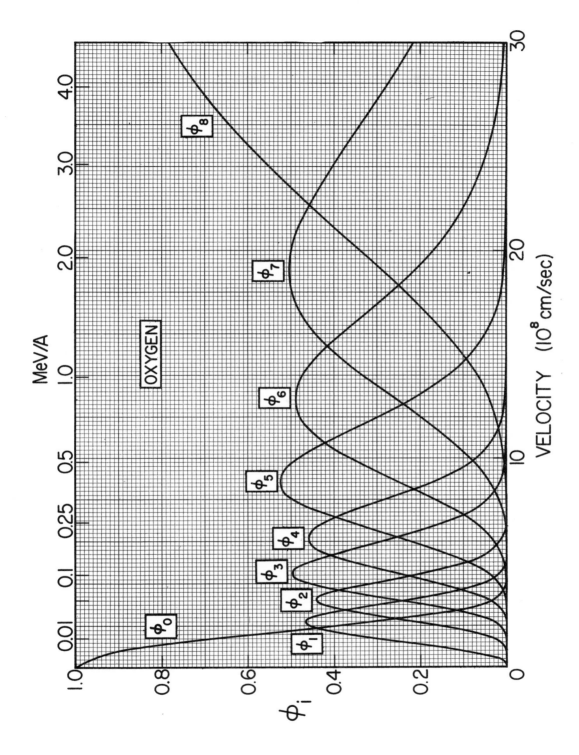

43

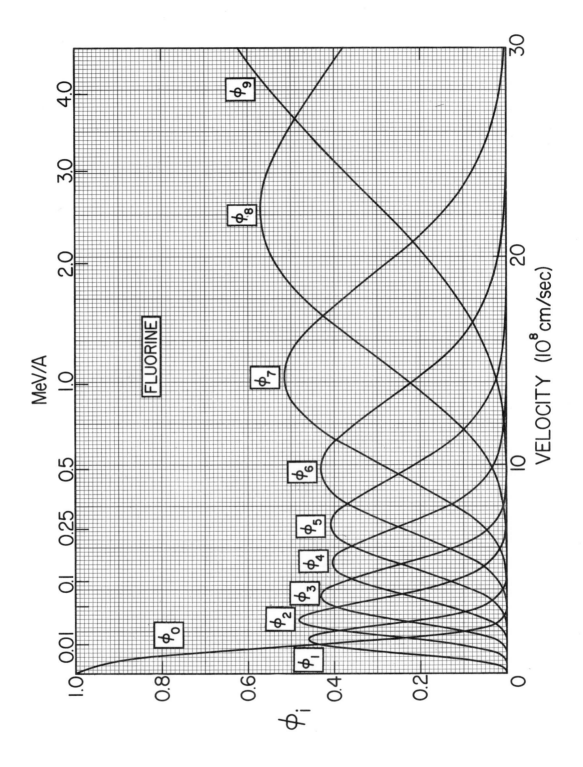

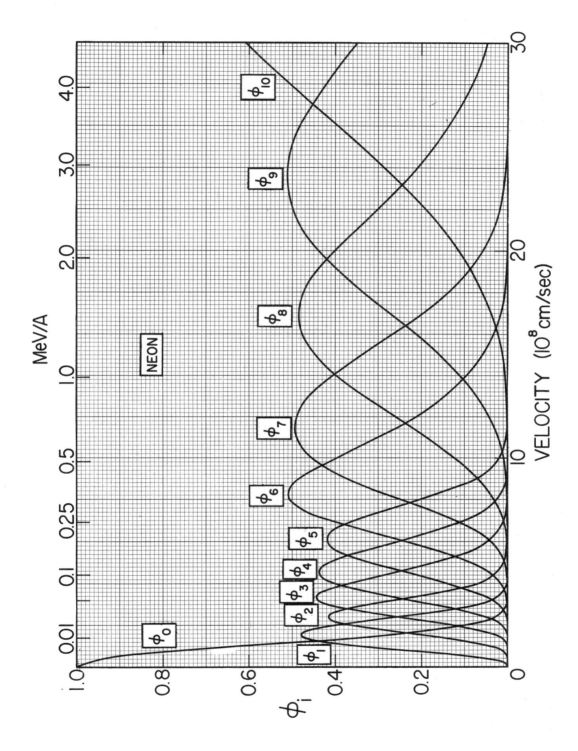

III. *Gamma-Ray Detection*

Figures 33–35. *Total detection efficiency for cylindrical* NaI(Tl) *crystals*

The curves in the accompanying three graphs give as functions of γ-ray energy the *total* detection efficiency for right-circular cylindrical NaI(Tl) crystals of various sizes. The parameter h is the distance between the (point) source and the front face of the crystal. The source is assumed to lie on the cylindrical axis of the crystal.

The curves for $1\frac{3}{4}''$ diam. $\times 2''$ crystals, $3''$ diam. $\times 3''$ crystals, and $5''$ diam. $\times 4''$ crystals were drawn from the calculated points of Vegors et al.,[1] and were extended to 20 MeV using the calculated points of Wolicki et al.[2] The curves for $5''$ diam. $\times 6''$ crystals were drawn from the calculated points of Rutledge,[3] for which the smallest h is 4.0 cm. The total detection efficiency for $5''$ diam. $\times 5''$ crystals may be determined by interpolating the curves for $5''$ diam. $\times 4''$ crystals and $5''$ diam. $\times 6''$ crystals. A few efficiency curves may also be found in Heath's Spectrum Catalogue.[4] An extensive set of efficiency curves for $1\frac{1}{2}''$ diam. $\times 1''$ crystals and $3''$ diam. $\times 3''$ crystals may be found in reference 5.

For peak-to-total detection efficiency ratios see Fig. 36.

[1] S. H. Vegors, Jr., L. L. Marsden and R. L. Heath, Calculated Efficiencies of Cylindrical Radiation Detectors, Phillips Petroleum Co. Report IDO-16370, unpublished (1958).

[2] E. A. Wolicki, R. Jastrow and F. Brooks, Calculated Efficiencies of NaI Crystals, U.S. Naval Research Laboratory Report NRL-4833, unpublished (1956).

[3] A. R. Rutledge, Finite Geometry Corrections to Gamma-Ray Angular Correlations Measured with 5 in. Diameter by 6 in. Long NaI(Tl) Crystals and with 3 in. Diameter by 3 in. Long NaI(Tl) Crystals, Chalk River Project Report CRP-851, unpublished (1959).

[4] R. L. Heath, Scintillation Spectrometry: Gamma-Ray Spectrum Catalogue, Phillips Petroleum Co. Report IDO-16408, unpublished (1957); also 2nd edition, Report IDO-16880, unpublished (1964).

[5] J. H. Neiler and P. R. Bell, in *Alpha-, Beta- and Gamma-Ray Spectroscopy*, ed. K. Siegbahn, Vol. 1 (North-Holland, Amsterdam, 1965) p. 245.

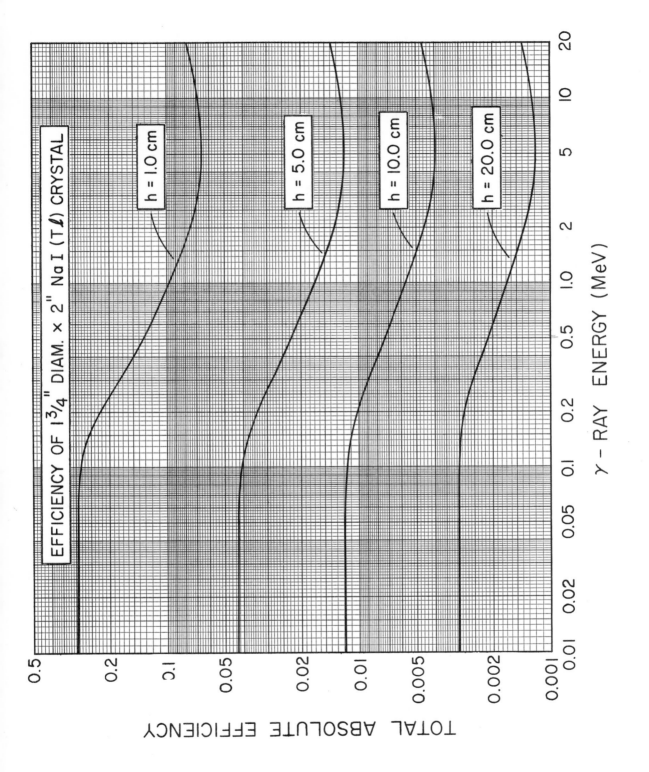

EFFICIENCY OF $1\frac{3}{4}$" DIAM. × 2" Na I (Tℓ) CRYSTAL

h = 1.0 cm

h = 5.0 cm

h = 10.0 cm

h = 20.0 cm

γ – RAY ENERGY (MeV)

TOTAL ABSOLUTE EFFICIENCY

49

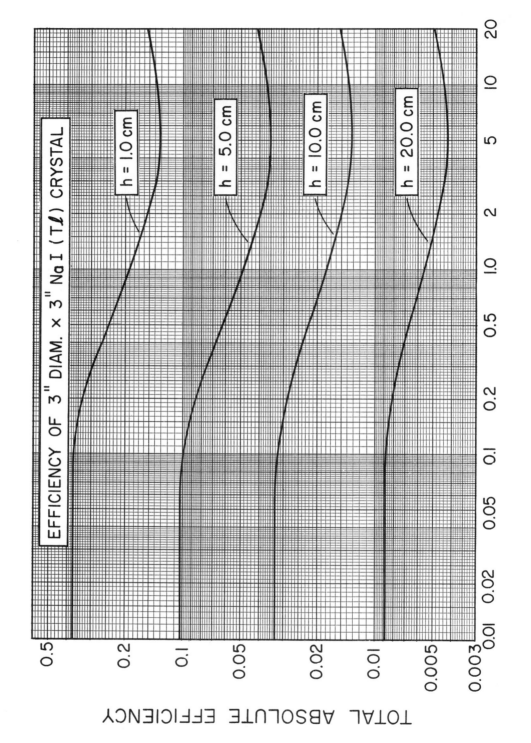

EFFICIENCY OF 3" DIAM. × 3" NaI (Tℓ) CRYSTAL

h = 1.0 cm
h = 5.0 cm
h = 10.0 cm
h = 20.0 cm

γ – RAY ENERGY (MeV)

TOTAL ABSOLUTE EFFICIENCY

50

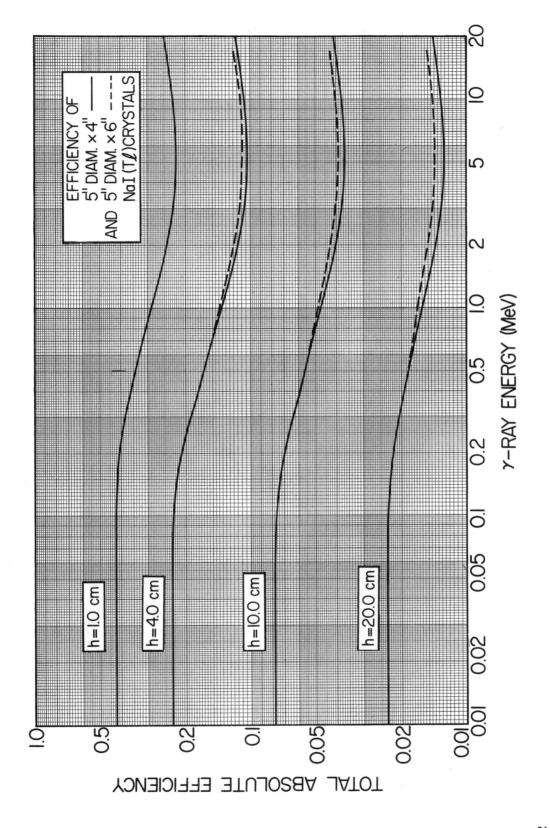

51

Figure 36. Peak-to-total detection efficiency ratios for cylindrical NaI(Tl) *crystals*

The curves given in Figs. 33, 34, and 35 show the *total* detection efficiency as functions of γ-ray energy for NaI(Tl) crystals of various sizes. The curves in the accompanying graph show the ratio of the detection efficiency for those interactions which give a contribution to the full-energy peak, to the total detection efficiency. The full-energy peak is assumed to be Gaussian in shape. The parameter h has the same meaning as in the three preceding figures and is the distance from the (point) source to the front face of the crystal.

The curves shown for $1\frac{3}{4}''$ diam. $\times 2''$ crystals and for $3''$ diam. $\times 3''$ crystals are adapted from those given by Heath.[1] The measurements of Hornyak et al.[2] were used to extend the curve for $3''$ diam. $\times 3''$ crystals from 3 MeV to 9 MeV. The curves shown for $5''$ diam. $\times 5''$ crystals are taken from the measurements of Heaton[3] for a source distance of 10 cm and from the measurements of Young et al.[4] for a source distance of 2 cm.

[1] R. L. Heath, Scintillation Spectrometry: Gamma-Ray Spectrum Catalogue, Phillips Petroleum Co. Report IDO-16408, unpublished (1957); also 2nd edition, Report IDO-16880, unpublished (1964).
[2] W. F. Hornyak, C. A. Ludemann and M. L. Roush, Nuclear Phys. 50 (1964) 424.
[3] H. T. Heaton, Investigation of the Response of Sodium Iodide Scintillators to Gamma Radiation, M. S. Thesis, University of Maryland, unpublished (1964).
[4] F. C. Young, H. T. Heaton, G. W. Phillips, P. D. Forsyth and J. B. Marion, Nuclear Instr. and Meth. 44 (1966) 109.

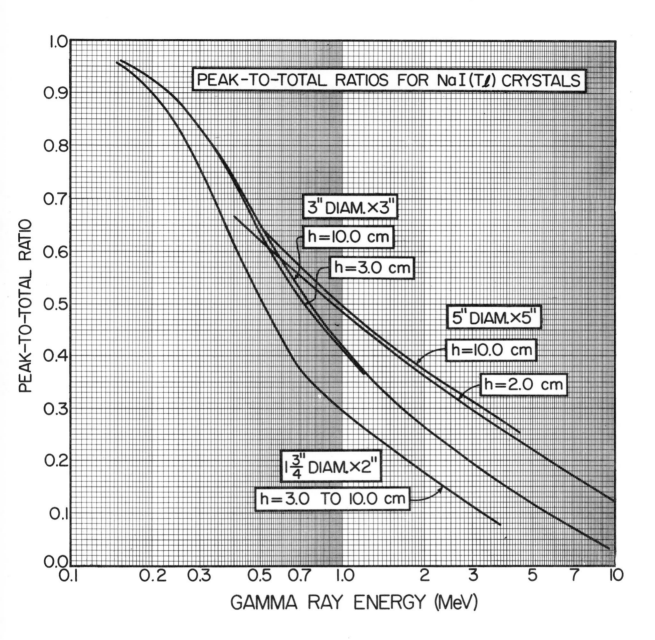

GAMMA RAY ENERGY (MeV)

53

Figure 37. Total efficiency and peak-to-total ratio for 2″ diam. × 2″ well-type NaI(Tl) crystals

The accompanying graph shows the total detection efficiency and the peak-to-total ratio for a well-type NaI(Tl) crystal. The crystal geometry is cylindrical, 2″ diam. × 2″, with a 1.125″ diam. hole on the cylinder axis and 1.50″ deep. The source is assumed to lie 0.2 cm from the bottom of the well and to be isotropic. No source attenuation is included.

The curves were drawn from the tables calculated by Snyder and Knoll[1] using a Monte Carlo technique. Measurements of absolute peak efficiencies for a similar well-type crystal may be found in reference 2. Calculations of absolute peak efficiencies for various geometries are given in reference 3.

[1] B. J. Snyder and G. F. Knoll, Nuclear Instr. and Meth. *40* (1966) 261.
[2] D. Redon, G. S. Mani, J. Delaunay-Olkowsky and C. Williamson, Nuclear Instr. and Meth. *26* (1964) 18.
[3] B. J. Snyder, Nuclear Instr. and Meth. *53* (1967) 313.

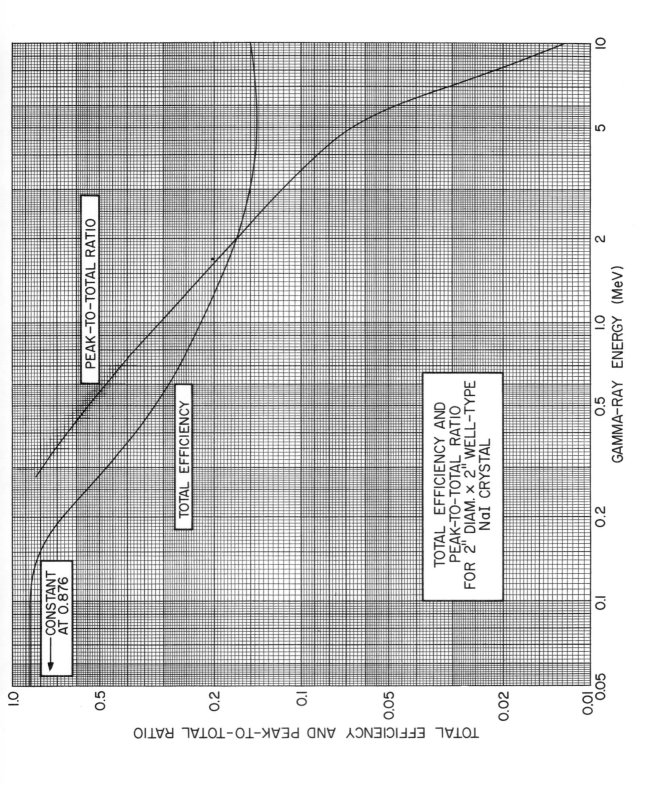

TOTAL EFFICIENCY AND PEAK-TO-TOTAL RATIO FOR 2" DIAM. x 2" WELL-TYPE NaI CRYSTAL

PEAK-TO-TOTAL RATIO

TOTAL EFFICIENCY

CONSTANT AT 0.876

GAMMA-RAY ENERGY (MeV)

TOTAL EFFICIENCY AND PEAK-TO-TOTAL RATIO

55

Figure 38. Energy of Compton electrons

In the Compton scattering of a γ ray, the electron which participates in the scattering process receives a fraction of the energy of the γ ray. The relationship between the scattered and primary photon energies is:

$$E'_\gamma/E_\gamma = [1+\alpha(1-\cos\theta)]^{-1} \tag{38.1}$$

where E_γ and E'_γ are the primary and scattered γ-ray energies, respectively, θ is the photon scattering angle, and $\alpha = E_\gamma/m_0 c^2$.

The energy of the struck electron in units of the primary energy is:

$$T/E_\gamma = \frac{\alpha(1-\cos\theta)}{1+\alpha(1-\cos\theta)}. \tag{38.2}$$

The accompanying graph shows T/E_γ as a function of E_γ for various photon scattering angles.

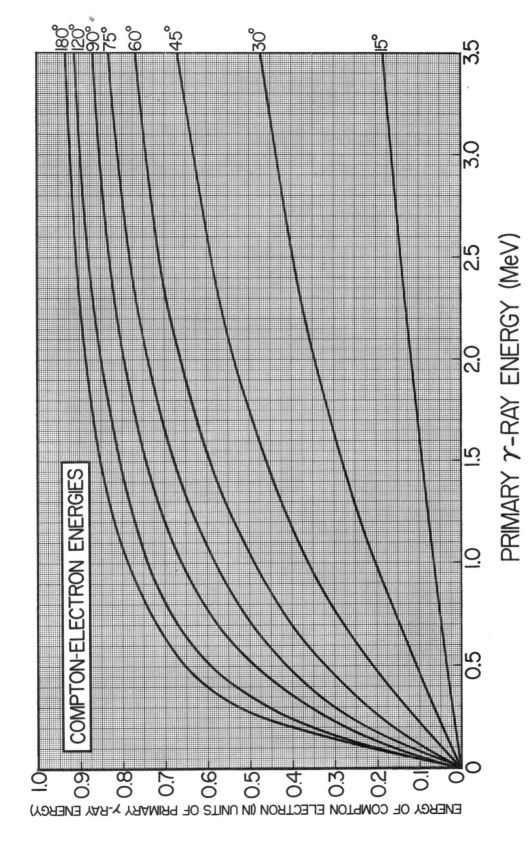

COMPTON-ELECTRON ENERGIES

PRIMARY γ-RAY ENERGY (MeV)

ENERGY OF COMPTON ELECTRON (IN UNITS OF PRIMARY γ-RAY ENERGY)

180°
120°
90°
75°
60°
45°
30°
15°

Figure 39. *Compton edge and backscatter peaks*

In the pulse-height distributions of Compton interactions of γ rays in scintillation detectors there are two prominent features usually present: (1) the Compton edge, which corresponds to the maximum energy that can be imparted to an electron by the γ ray, and (2) the backscatter peak, which corresponds to the absorption of a photon which has been scattered through 180° in the material surrounding the detector.

The energy of the Compton edge is given by:

$$E_C = E_\gamma/(1 + m_0 c^2/2E_\gamma) \tag{39.1}$$

where E_γ is the energy of the incident γ ray. The energy of the backscatter peak is given by:

$$E_b = E_\gamma - E_C = m_0 c^2/(2 + m_0 c^2/E_\gamma) . \tag{39.2}$$

The quantities E_C and E_b are shown in the graphs as functions of E_γ for both low- and high-energy regions.

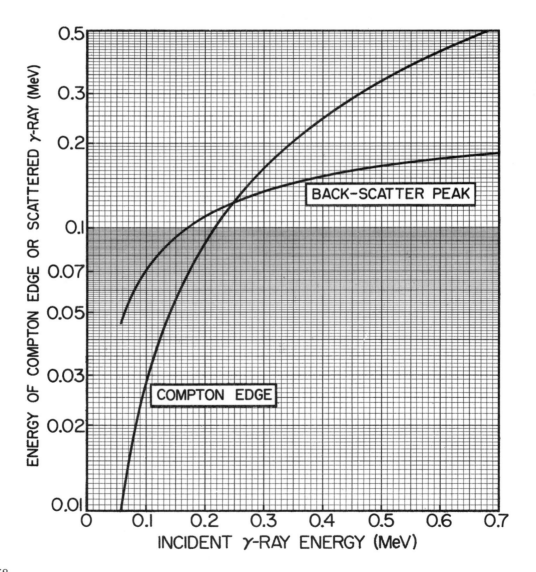

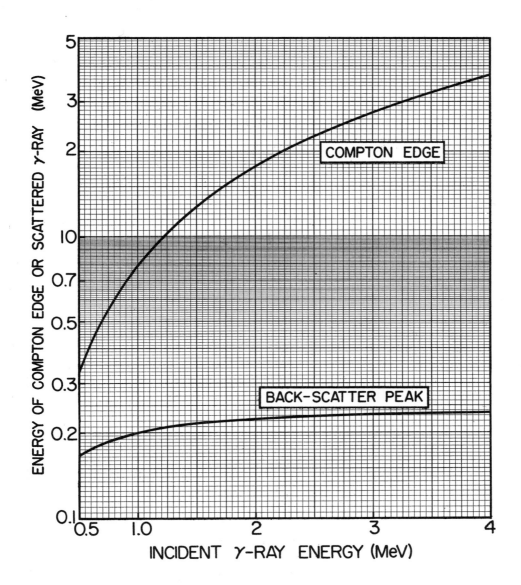

Figure 40.   Average K *X-ray energies vs. Z*

If an electron is removed from the K shell of an atom, the vacancy thus created will be filled by an electron from a higher shell and an X-ray will be emitted. The accompanying graphs shows the average K X-ray energy as a function of atomic number. The curve was drawn through points listed by Nijgh et al.[1]

[1] G. J. Nijgh, A. H. Wapstra and R. van Lieshout, *Nuclear Spectroscopy Tables* (North-Holland, Amsterdam, 1959) p. 81.

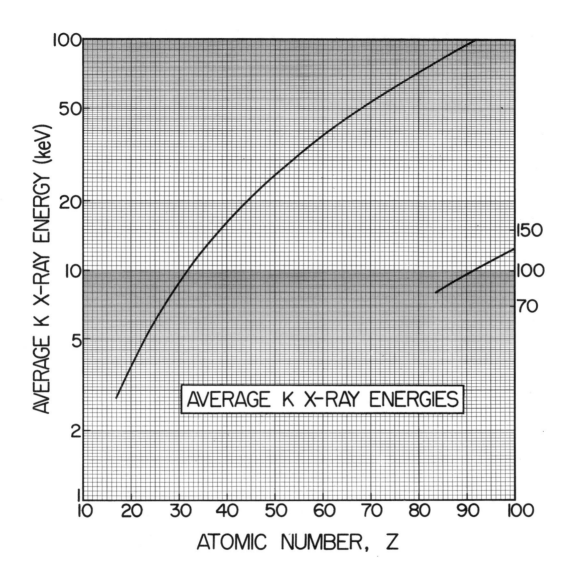

AVERAGE K X-RAY ENERGIES

61

Figure 41. *Absorption coefficients for sodium iodide*

The accompanying graph shows the absorption coefficients for γ rays in sodium iodide as functions of γ-ray energy. The contributions to the absorption coefficient from photoelectric, Compton, and pair production processes are also given. The Compton and total absorption curves do not include contributions from coherent (Thomson) scattering. These curves are useful for estimating the relative efficiency of NaI detectors for various γ-ray interaction processes.

The curves were plotted from the tables of Grodstein.[1]

---

[1] G. W. Grodstein, *X-Ray Attenuation Coefficients from 10 keV to 100 MeV*, National Bureau of Standards Circular 583 (1957).

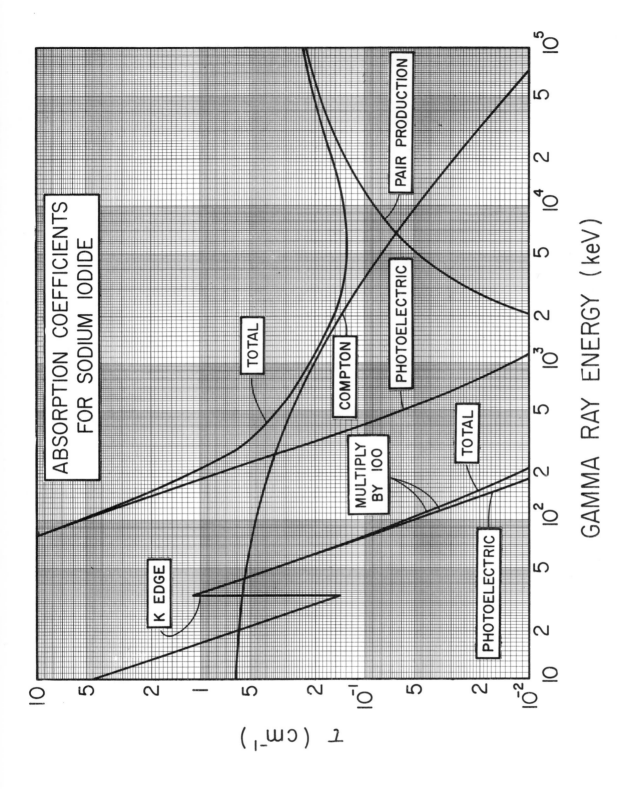

ABSORPTION COEFFICIENTS FOR SODIUM IODIDE

TOTAL

COMPTON

PHOTOELECTRIC

PAIR PRODUCTION

K EDGE

MULTIPLY BY 100

TOTAL

PHOTOELECTRIC

GAMMA RAY ENERGY (keV)

τ (cm^{-1})

Figure 42.   Absorption coefficients for germanium

The accompanying graph shows the absorption coefficients for γ rays in germanium as functions of γ-ray energy. The contribution to the absorption coefficient from photoelectric, Compton, and pair production processes are also given. The Compton and total absorption curves do not include contributions from coherent (Thomson) scattering. These curves are useful for estimating the relative efficiency of lithium-drifted germanium detectors for various γ-ray interaction processes.

The curves were plotted from the tables of Storm et al.[1] Efficiency curves for two Ge(Li) detectors are given in the following figure.

[1]   E. Storm, E. Gilbert and H. Israel, Gamma-Ray Absorption Coefficients for Elements 1 through 100 Derived from the Theoretical Values of the National Bureau of Standards, Los Alamos Scientific Laboratory Report LA-2237, unpublished (1958).

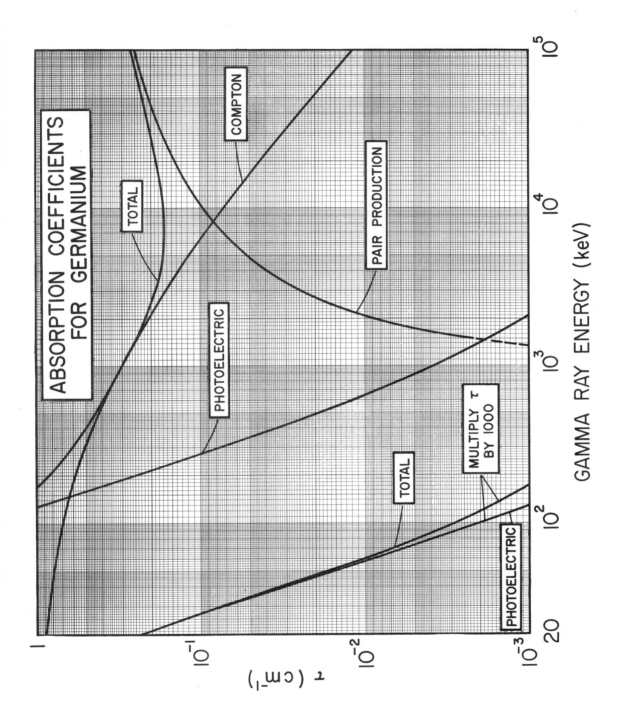

ABSORPTION COEFFICIENTS FOR GERMANIUM

GAMMA RAY ENERGY (keV)

τ (cm^{-1})

TOTAL

COMPTON

PAIR PRODUCTION

PHOTOELECTRIC

TOTAL

MULTIPLY τ BY 1000

PHOTOELECTRIC

Figure 43. Efficiency of lithium-drifted germanium detectors

In contrast to the case for NaI detectors, lithium-drifted germanium detectors are not available in universally accepted standard sizes and shapes. Total absolute efficiencies and other γ-ray response characteristics, such as peak-to-total ratios and double-escape pair peak efficiencies, have been calculated by various authors[1-5] for various detector sizes and shapes. Some measurements of these properties have also been made.[6-12] Since Ge(Li) detectors are usually much smaller than NaI detectors, these properties are more sensitive to the geometrical arrangement of the source and detector. A method for obtaining the relative total-energy-peak efficiency over the γ-ray energy range 500 to 1500 keV has been given by Freeman and Jenkin.[11]

The graph opposite shows the measurements of Cline and Heath[12] of the total absolute peak efficiency and double-escape pair peak efficiency for a $2.5 \text{ cm}^2 \times 4$ mm (1.0 cm^3) planar Ge(Li) detector and the total absolute peak efficiency, single-escape, and double-escape pair peak efficiencies for a 26 mm diam. $\times$ 30 mm long $\times$ 7 mm drift (12 cm^3) coaxial Ge(Li) detector. These measurements are for a point source located 3 cm from the front of the detector along the central axis.

Angular correlation correction factors for square Ge(Li) detectors of various sizes have been calculated by Avida et al.[13]

[1] H. P. Hotz, J. M. Mathiesen and J. P. Hurley, Nuclear Instr. and Meth. *37* (1965) 93.
[2] E. S. Fry, J. M. Palms and R. B. Day, Calculation of the Pulse-Height Response of Ge(Li) Semiconductor Counters, Los Alamos Scientific Laboratory Report LA-3456, unpublished (1966).
[3] K. M. Wainio and G. F. Knoll, Nuclear Instr. and Meth. *44* (1966) 213.
[4] N. V. De Castro Faria and R. J. A. Levesque, Nuclear Instr. and Meth. *46* (1967) 325.
[5] J. L. Black and W. Gruhle, Nuclear Instr. and Meth. *46* (1967) 213.
[6] G. T. Ewan and A. J. Tavendale, Can. J. Phys. *42* (1964) 2286.
[7] D. E. Alburger and K. W. Jones, Phys. Rev. *149* (1966) 743.
[8] H. L. Malm, A. J. Tavendale and I. L. Fowler, Can. J. Phys. *43* (1965) 1173.
[9] D. C. Camp, University of California, Lawrence Radiation Laboratory (Livermore), and private communication.
[10] J. E. Draper, R. O. Mead and R. A. Warner, Nuclear Phys. *A95* (1967) 209.
[11] J. M. Freeman and J. G. Jenkin, Nuclear Instr. and Meth. *43* (1966) 269.
[12] J. M. Cline and R. L. Heath, Gamma-Ray Spectrometry of Neutron Deficient Isotopes, Annual Progress Report IDO-17222, unpublished (1966); and W. L. Weiss, private communication.
[13] R. Avida, U. Atzmony and I. Unna, Nuclear Instr. and Meth. *46* (1967) 350.

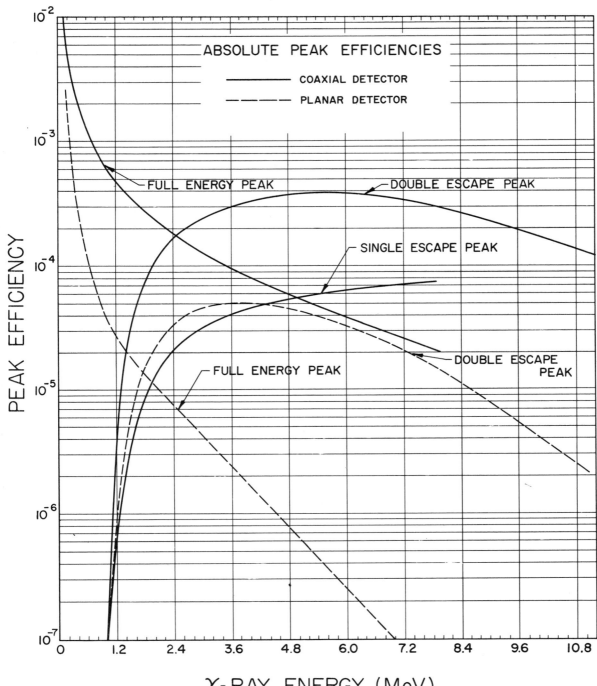

67

Figure 44.   Total γ-ray attenuation in lead

The accompanying graph gives the total attenuation coefficient for a *narrow* γ-ray beam in lead. The curve is based on the calculations of the various interaction coefficients made by Storm et al.,[1] and includes the contribution of coherent (Thomson) scattering.

[1] E. Storm, E. Gilbert and H. Israel, Gamma-Ray Absorption Coefficients for the Elements 1 through 100 Derived from the Theoretical Values of the National Bureau of Standards, Los Alamos Scientific Laboratory Report LA-2237, unpublished (1958).

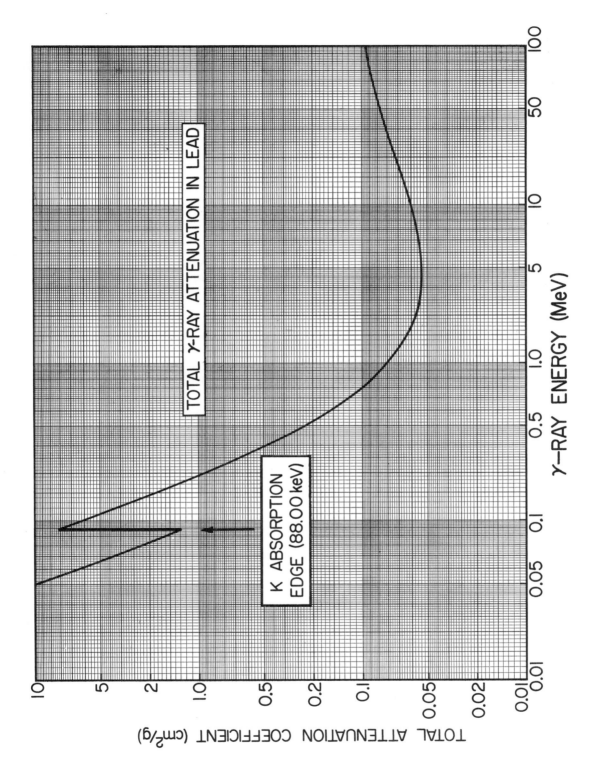

TOTAL γ-RAY ATTENUATION IN LEAD

K ABSORPTION
EDGE (88.00 keV)

γ-RAY ENERGY (MeV)

TOTAL ATTENUATION COEFFICIENT (cm²/g)

69

Figures 45–54. Angular correlation correction factors for cylindrical NaI(Tl) *crystals*

In the measurements of angular correlations of γ rays with detectors of finite size, geometrical corrections must be applied in order to deduce the true correlation. Rose[1] has derived formulas for these corrections, but computations must usually be performed using electronic computers. Such calculations have been made for NaI crystals of various sizes and for various source-to-detector distances. Figs. 45 through 54 show the correction factors for some selected geometries.

If the true angular correlation of the γ ray with respect to some fixed axis is given by

$$W(\theta) = \sum_{l=0}^{L} a_l P_l(\cos \theta) \qquad (45.1)$$

where $P_l(\cos \theta)$ is the Legendre polynomial of order l, then the measured correlation, when fitted by a similar expansion, will have coefficients b_l given by

$$b_l/b_0 = (J_l/J_0)(a_l/a_0). \qquad (45.2)$$

In the event that a γ–γ correlation is measured, then the correction factors are products of J_l/J_0 for the two detectors, and the measured distribution function $\overline{W}(\theta)$ can be written as

$$\overline{W}(\theta) = \sum_{l=0}^{L} [J_l(1)/J_0(1)][J_l(2)/J_0(2)] a_l P_l(\cos \theta) \qquad (45.3)$$

where $J_l(1)$ and $J_l(2)$ refer to the first and second crystals, respectively. The accompanying six graphs show the factors J_2/J_0 and J_4/J_0 for $1\frac{3}{4}''$ diam. $\times 2''$ crystals, $3''$ diam. $\times 3''$ crystals, $5''$ diam. $\times 4''$ crystals, and $5''$ diam. $\times 6''$ crystals. The parameter h is the distance between the (point) source and the front face of the crystal. The source is assumed to lie on the cylindrical axis of the crystal and the detectors are assumed uncollimated.

The correlation corrections shown in Figs. 45–50 were computed with the assumption that all pulses produced in the crystal by the γ ray interacting in any of the three possible modes (Compton scattering, photoelectric effect, and pair production) are detected. The curves in these graphs were plotted from the tables of references 1, 2, and 3. Similar calculations for other geometries have been made by Stanford and Rivers.[4]

Frequently, only the number of counts in the full-energy peak is measured in angular correlation experiments. Then the previous correction factors J_l/J_0 represent only a lower limit for the true correction factors because γ rays interacting at the edges of the crystal are less likely to contribute to the full-energy peak than those interacting at the center. Angular correlation correction factors based on detection of the full-energy peak have been calculated only for a few geometries. Figures 51–54 show the factors J_2/J_0 and J_4/J_0 for 3″ diam. × 3″ crystals, and 5″ diam. × 6″ crystals. The curves in these figures were plotted from the tables of reference 5. The curves for 3″ diam. × 3″ crystals for source-to-detector distances of 6 cm and 10 cm were extended from 0.3 MeV to 0.1 MeV using the calculations of Yates.[6]

Similar angular correlation correction factors have been calculated by Twin and Wilmott,[7] and have been experimentally measured by Reich and Douglas,[8] and Herskind and Yoshizawa.[9] Reviews of angular correlation correction factors are given in references 10 and 11.

[1] H. I. West, Jr., Angular Correlation Factors via the Method of Rose, University of California Radiation Laboratory (Livermore) Report UCRL-5451, unpublished (1959).

[2] A. R. Rutledge, Finite Geometry Corrections to Gamma-Ray Angular Correlations Measured with 5 in. Diameter by 6 in. Long NaI(Tl) Crystals and with 3 in. Diameter by 3 in. Long NaI(Tl) Crystals, Chalk River Project Report CRP-851, unpublished (1959).

[3] H. E. Gove and A. R. Rutledge, Finite Geometry Corrections to Gamma-Ray Angular Correlations Measured with 5 in. Diameter by 4 in. Long NaI(Tl) Crystals, Chalk River Project Report CRP-755, unpublished (1958).

[4] A. L. Stanford, Jr. and W. K. Rivers, Jr., Rev. Sci. Instr. *30* (1959) 719.

[5] C. R. Gossett and C. M. Davisson, quoted by A. J. Ferguson, *Angular Correlation Methods in Gamma-Ray Spectroscopy* (North-Holland, Amsterdam, 1965) pp. 195–6.

[6] M. J. L. Yates, Nuclear Instr. and Meth. *23* (1963) 152.

[7] P. J. Twin and J. C. Willmott, Nuclear Instr. and Meth. *22* (1963) 109.

[8] C. W. Reich and J. H. Douglas, Nuclear Instr. and Meth. *35* (1965) 67.

[9] B. Herskind and Y. Yoshizawa, Nuclear Instr. and Meth. *27* (1964) 104.

[10] M. J. L. Yates, in *Perturbed Angular Correlations*, eds. E. Karlsson, E. Matthias and K. Siegbahn (North-Holland, Amsterdam, 1964) p. 453.

[11] A. J. Ferguson, *Angular Correlation Methods in Gamma-Ray Spectroscopy* (North-Holland, Amsterdam, 1966).

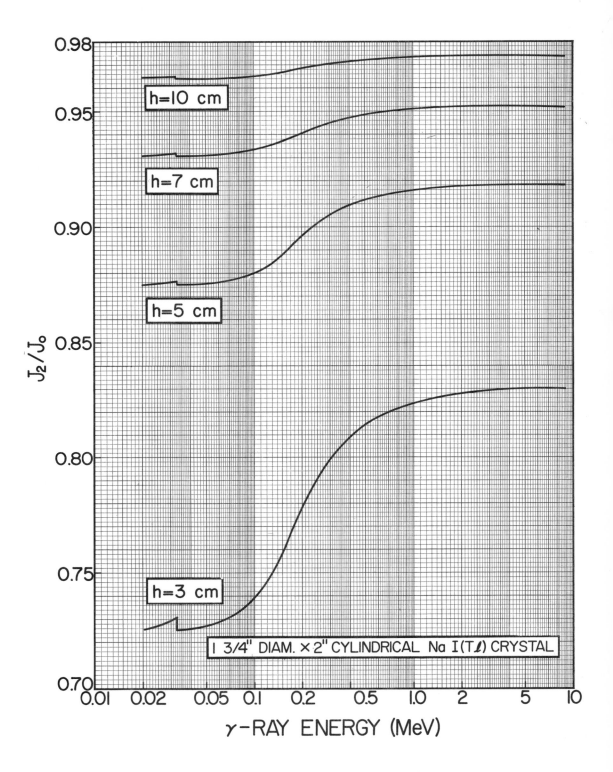

h=10 cm

h=7 cm

h=5 cm

h=3 cm

1 3/4" DIAM. × 2" CYLINDRICAL NaI(Tℓ) CRYSTAL

J_2/J_o

γ-RAY ENERGY (MeV)

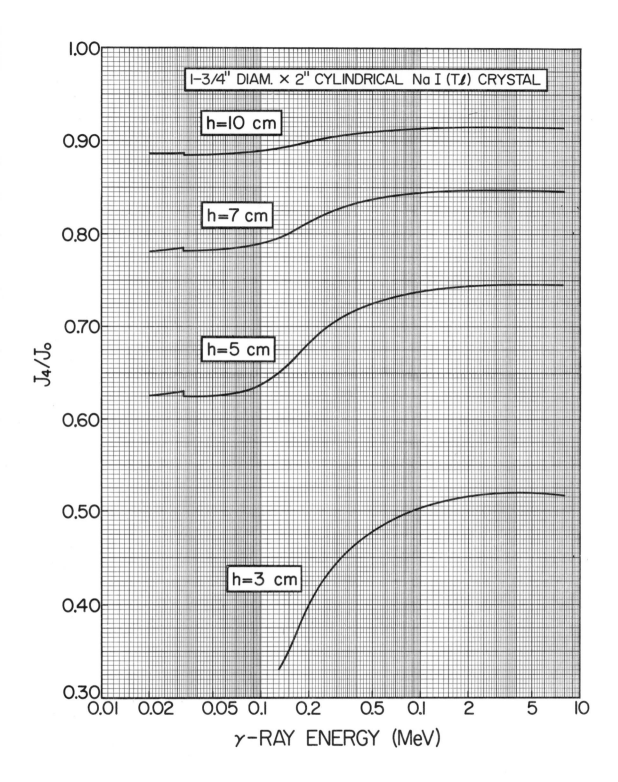

73

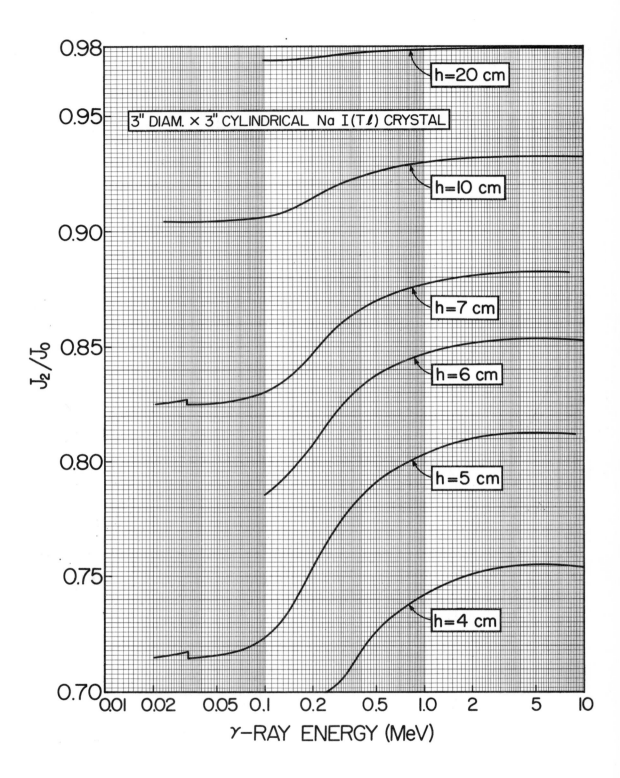

3" DIAM. × 3" CYLINDRICAL Na I(Tℓ) CRYSTAL

h=20 cm

h=10 cm

h=7 cm

h=6 cm

h=5 cm

h=4 cm

J_2/J_0

γ−RAY ENERGY (MeV)

74

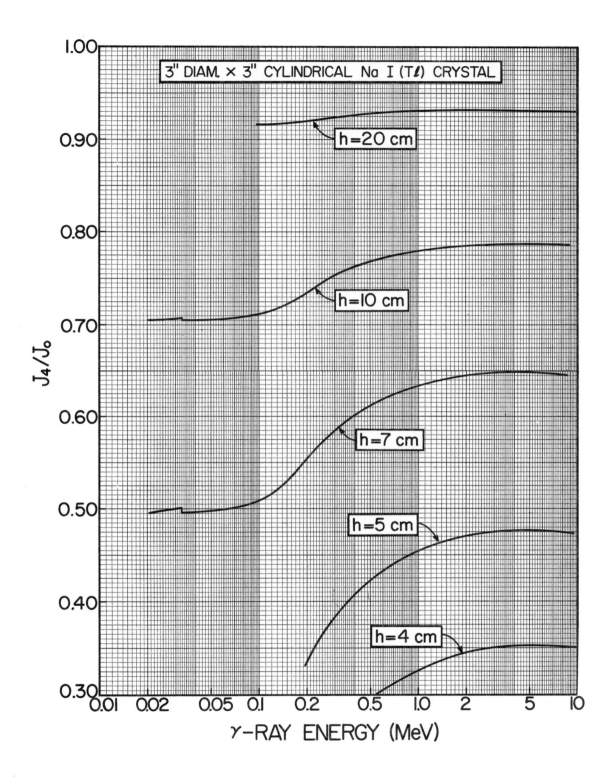

3" DIAM. × 3" CYLINDRICAL Na I (Tℓ) CRYSTAL

h=20 cm

h=10 cm

h=7 cm

h=5 cm

h=4 cm

J_4/J_0

γ-RAY ENERGY (MeV)

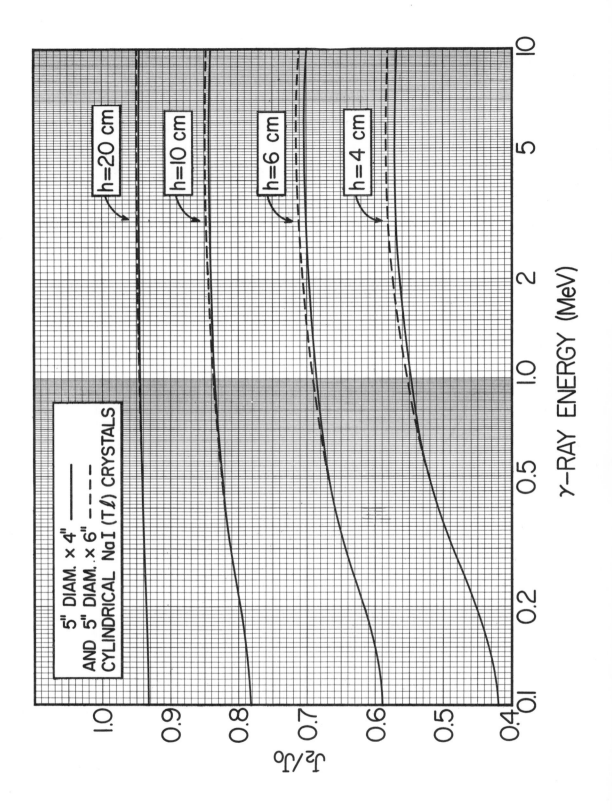

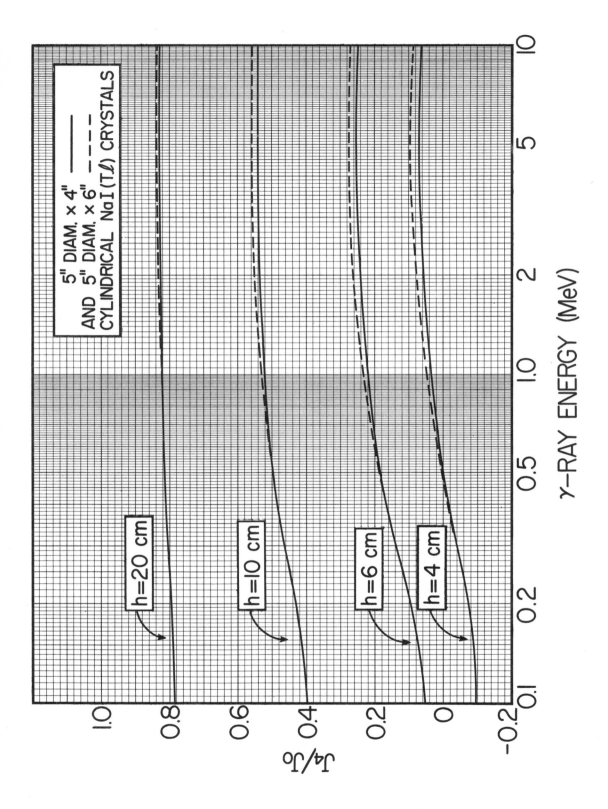

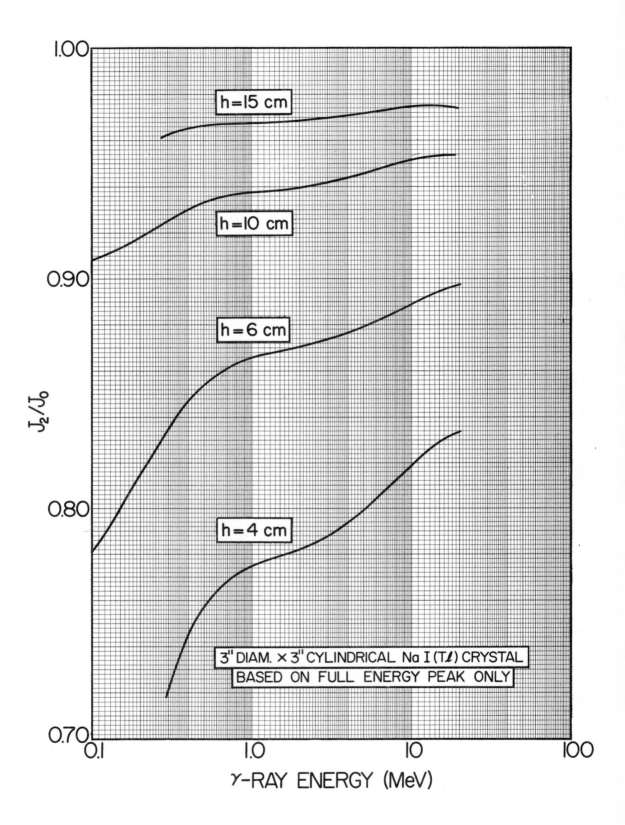

h = 15 cm

h = 10 cm

h = 6 cm

h = 4 cm

3" DIAM. × 3" CYLINDRICAL Na I (Tl) CRYSTAL
BASED ON FULL ENERGY PEAK ONLY

J_2/J_0

γ-RAY ENERGY (MeV)

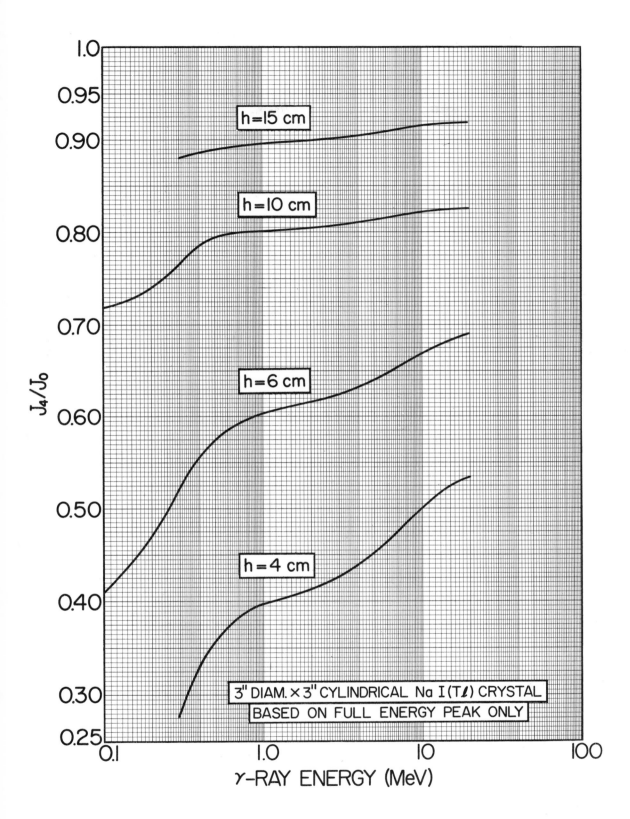

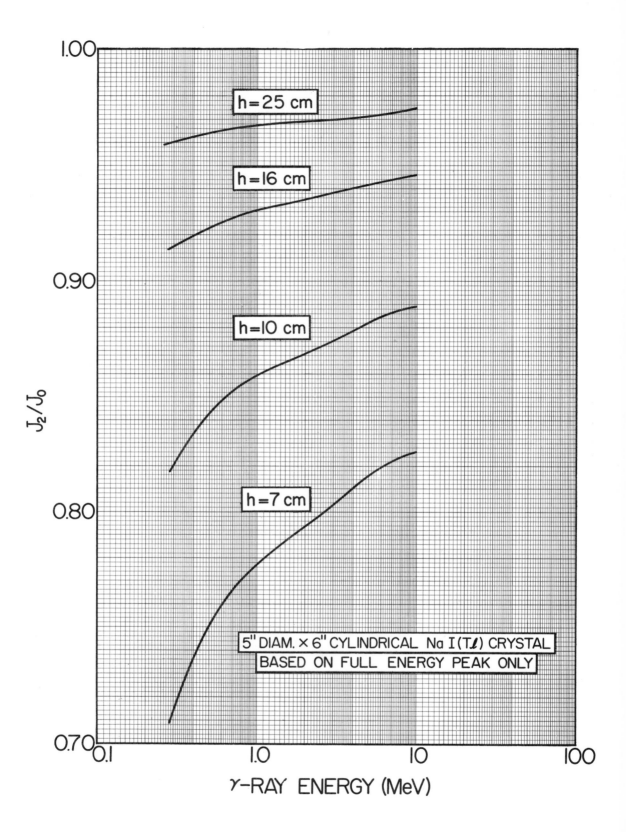

h=25 cm

h=16 cm

h=10 cm

h=7 cm

5" DIAM. × 6" CYLINDRICAL Na I(Tℓ) CRYSTAL
BASED ON FULL ENERGY PEAK ONLY

J_2/J_0

γ-RAY ENERGY (MeV)

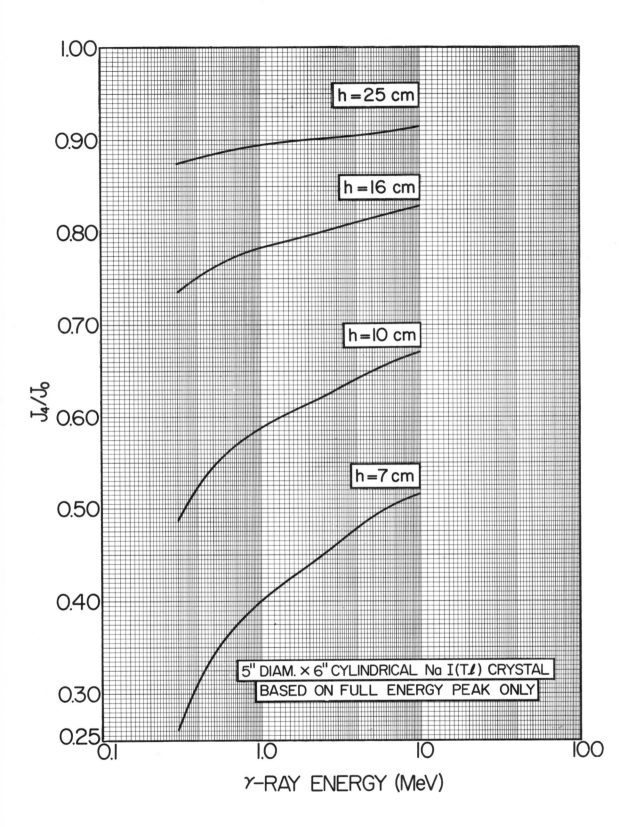

81

IV. *Penetrability and Shift Functions*

Figure 55.   Values of ϱ and η for protons[1]

Coulomb wave functions are usually calculated in terms of the dimensionless parameters ϱ and η:

$$\varrho = kR \tag{55.1}$$

$$= 0.2187\mu R\sqrt{E/A_1}, \quad \text{for} \quad \begin{cases} R \text{ in fm} \\ E \text{ in MeV} \end{cases} \tag{55.1a}$$

$$\eta = Z_1 Z_2 e^2 / \hbar v \tag{55.2}$$

$$= 0.1575 Z_1 Z_2 \sqrt{A_1/E} \tag{55.2a}$$

where E and v are the laboratory energy and the laboratory velocity, respectively, of the incident particle; subscripts 1 and 2 refer to the incident and target particles, respectively, and A_1, A_2 and Z_1, Z_2 are the atomic masses (amu) and atomic numbers of the particles. The reduced mass is

$$\mu = \frac{A_1 A_2}{A_1 + A_2}. \tag{55.3}$$

The interaction radius is $R = R_0(A_1^{\frac{1}{3}} + A_2^{\frac{1}{3}})$, and $R_0 = 1.40$ fm is chosen.

The accompanying graph shows ϱ and η as functions of E and Z_2 for protons. The rough values of ϱ and η that can be read from this graph are useful for obtaining penetrabilities from the following graphs. If more accurate values are required, these can be calculated from the expressions above or can be read from Table 10.

Because ϱ is a function of A_1, A_2, whereas η is a function of Z_1, Z_2, in constructing the graph it was assumed that the target nucleus consists of equal numbers of protons and neutrons, i.e., $A_2 = 2Z_2$. Hence, the graph is quite accurate for $Z_2 \lesssim 20$ but deviations occur for higher Z_2. The error is only about 5 per cent, however, for protons bombarding Sn^{120} ($Z_2 = 50$).

If ϱ, η values are desired for an *outgoing* channel, the following expressions should be used:

$$\bar{\varrho} = 0.2187\bar{R}\sqrt{\bar{\mu}\left(\frac{\mu E}{A_1} + Q\right)} \tag{55.4}$$

$$\bar{\eta} = 0.1575\bar{Z}_3\bar{Z}_4\sqrt{\frac{\bar{\mu}}{(\mu E/A_1) + Q}} \tag{55.5}$$

where the barred quantities refer to the *outgoing* channel.

Values of ϱ, η for bombarding particles other than protons may be obtained from the graph by using the table below in which the incident particle is of the same bombarding energy as the proton.

Particle	η	$\log \eta$	ϱ
p	η_p	$\log \eta_p$	ϱ_p
d	$\sqrt{2}\eta_p$	$\log \eta_p + 0.15$	$\sqrt{2}\varrho_p \left(\dfrac{A+1}{A+2}\right)\left(\dfrac{\beta+1.26}{\beta+1}\right)$
t	$\sqrt{3}\eta_p$	$\log \eta_p + 0.24$	$\sqrt{3}\varrho_p \left(\dfrac{A+1}{A+3}\right)\left(\dfrac{\beta+1.44}{\beta+1}\right)$
He^3	$2\sqrt{3}\eta_p$	$\log \eta_p + 0.54$	$\sqrt{3}\varrho_p \left(\dfrac{A+1}{A+3}\right)\left(\dfrac{\beta+1.44}{\beta+1}\right)$
α	$4\eta_p$	$\log \eta_p + 0.60$	$2\varrho_p \left(\dfrac{A+1}{A+4}\right)\left(\dfrac{\beta+1.59}{\beta+1}\right)$

A_2 has been abbreviated to A, and $\beta = (A_2)^{\frac{1}{3}}$.

[1] This material is adapted from that given by W. T. Sharp, H. E. Gove and E. B. Paul, Graphs of Coulomb Wave Functions, 2nd edition, Chalk River Report AECL-268, unpublished (1955).

84

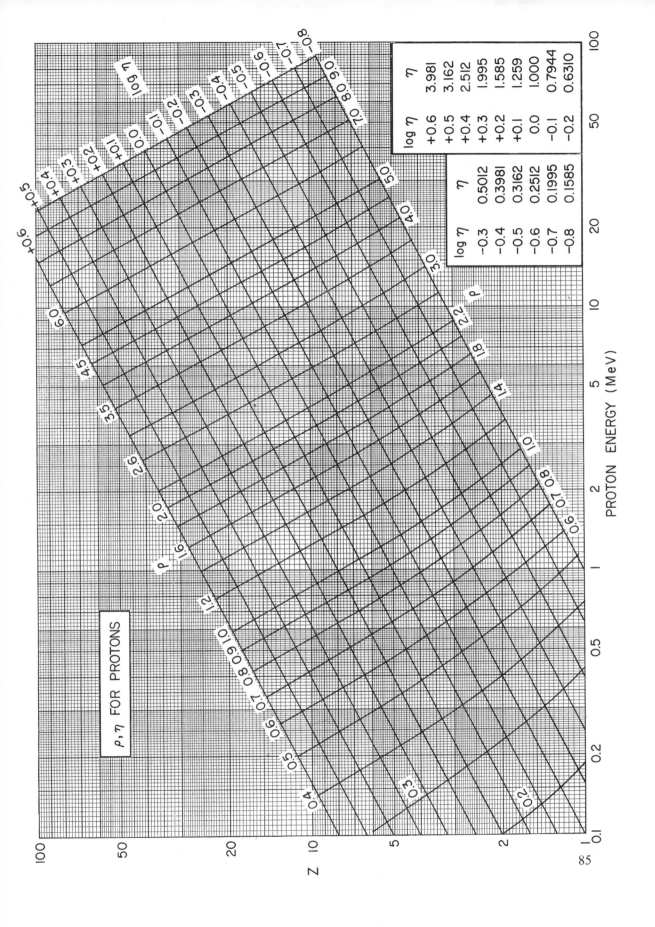

ρ, η FOR PROTONS

log η	η
+0.6	3.981
+0.5	3.162
+0.4	2.512
+0.3	1.995
+0.2	1.585
+0.1	1.259
0.0	1.000
-0.1	0.7944
-0.2	0.6310

log η	η
-0.3	0.5012
-0.4	0.3981
-0.5	0.3162
-0.6	0.2512
-0.7	0.1995
-0.8	0.1585

PROTON ENERGY (MeV)

Z

Figures 56–60.   Charged-particle penetrability functions

This graph and the following graphs show penetrability functions for $l=0$ through $l=4$ as functions of the parameters ϱ and η (see the preceding figure).

The total width Γ of a level is the sum of the partial widths:

$$\Gamma = \sum_{\alpha s l} \Gamma_{\alpha s l} \tag{56.1}$$

where α, s, and l specify the channel, the channel spin, and the relative angular momentum of the particles, respectively. The general expression connecting a partial width $\Gamma_{\alpha s l}$ and the corresponding reduced width $\gamma_{\alpha s l}^2$ is given by[1]

$$\Gamma_{\alpha s l} = \frac{2\varrho_\alpha \gamma_{\alpha s l}^2}{A_{\alpha l}^2 \left(1 + \sum_{s l} \gamma_{\alpha s l}^2 \dot{S}_{\alpha l}\right)} \tag{56.2}$$

where $A_{\alpha l}^2 = F_{\alpha l}^2 + G_{\alpha l}^2$ is the *penetration function* (F and G are the regular and irregular solutions of the Coulomb wave equation), and where $\dot{S}_{\alpha l}$ is the derivative with respect to energy (and evaluated at the resonance energy E_R and at a fixed interaction radius R_α) of the *shift function* $S_{\alpha l}$:

$$S_{\alpha l} = \frac{\varrho_\alpha}{2A_{\alpha l}^2} \frac{\mathrm{d}}{\mathrm{d}\varrho_\alpha}(A_{\alpha l}^2) . \tag{56.3}$$

The denominator of eq. (56.2) differs from $A_{\alpha l}^2$ only in the event that $\gamma_{\alpha s l}^2$ is larger than about 20 per cent of the Wigner limit, $3\hbar^2/2\mu R^2$ (see Table 10).

The accompanying graph and those following show ϱ/A_l^2 for $l=0, 1, 2, 3, 4$ and were plotted from the tables of Lal et al.[2] These tables also contain the material necessary to compute S_l. ($\dot{S}_l$ can usually be obtained with sufficient accuracy by graphical methods from a plot of S_l as a function of energy.[3])

The tables of Lal et al.[2] are probably the most useful, but others are also available.[4-6] Collections of graphs have also been prepared.[3,7]

In the figures, note the change of scale at $\varrho=2$.

[1] The theory of resonance reactions can be found in a number of recent articles, for example, G. Breit, in *Handbuch der Physik*, ed. E. Flügge, Vol. 41/1 (Springer-Verlag, Berlin, 1959) p. 1;
A. M. Lane and R. G. Thomas, Revs. Modern Phys. 30 (1958) 257;
E. Vogt, in *Nuclear Reactions*, eds. P. M. Endt and M. Demeur, Vol. I (North-Holland, Amsterdam, 1959) p. 215;
H. B. Willard, L. C. Biedenharn, P. Huber and E. Baumgartner, in *Fast Neutron Physics*, eds. J. B. Marion and J. L. Fowler, Part II (Wiley-Interscience, New York, 1963) p. 1217.
[2] M. Lal, H. Maximchuk and J. T. Sample, Coulomb and Related Functions, University of Alberta Report, unpublished (1962).
[3] See, for example, H. E. Gove, in *Nuclear Reactions*, eds. P. M. Endt and M. Demeur, Vol. I (North-Holland, Amsterdam, 1959) p. 259.
[4] I. Block, M. H. Hull, Jr., A. A. Broyles, W. G. Bouricius, B. E. Freeman and G. Breit, Revs. Modern Phys. 23 (1951) 147.
[5] J. P. Schiffer, Tables of Charged Particle Penetrabilities, Argonne National Laboratory Report ANL-5739, unpublished (1957).
[6] A. Tubis, Tables of Nonrelativistic Coulomb Wave Functions, Los Alamos Scientific Laboratory Report LA-2150, unpublished (1958). These tables are for $l=0$ only.
[7] W. T. Sharp, H. E. Gove and E. B. Paul, Graphs of Coulomb Functions, 2nd edition, Chalk River Laboratory Report AECL-268, unpublished (1955).

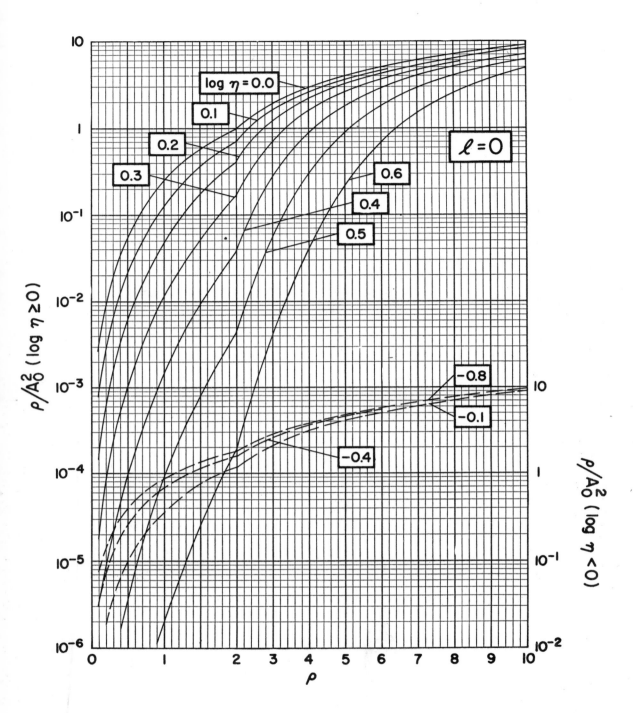

87

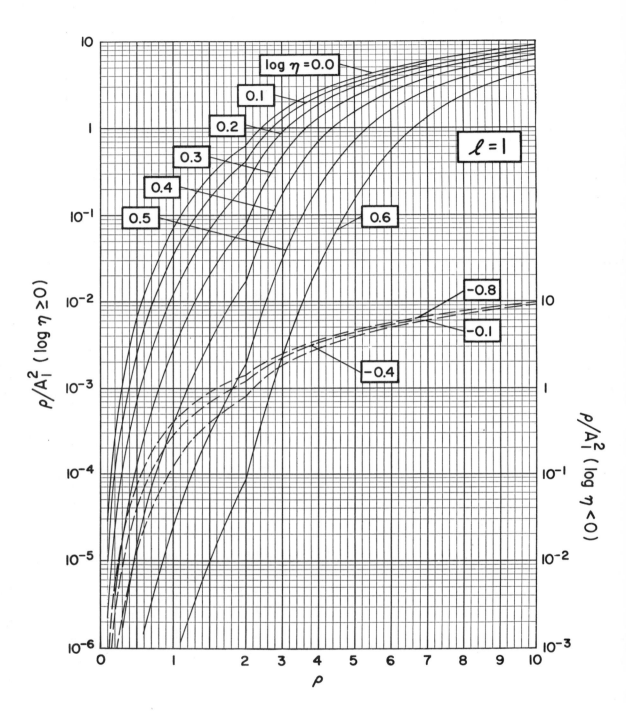

88

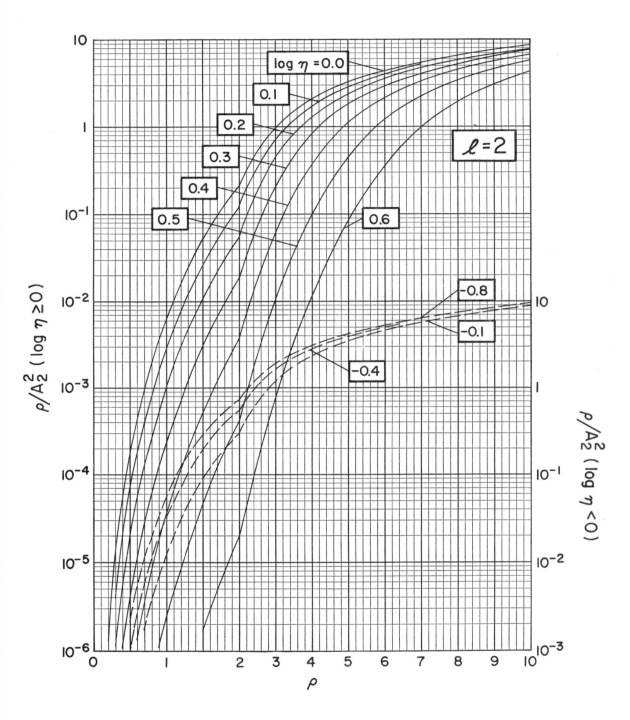

89

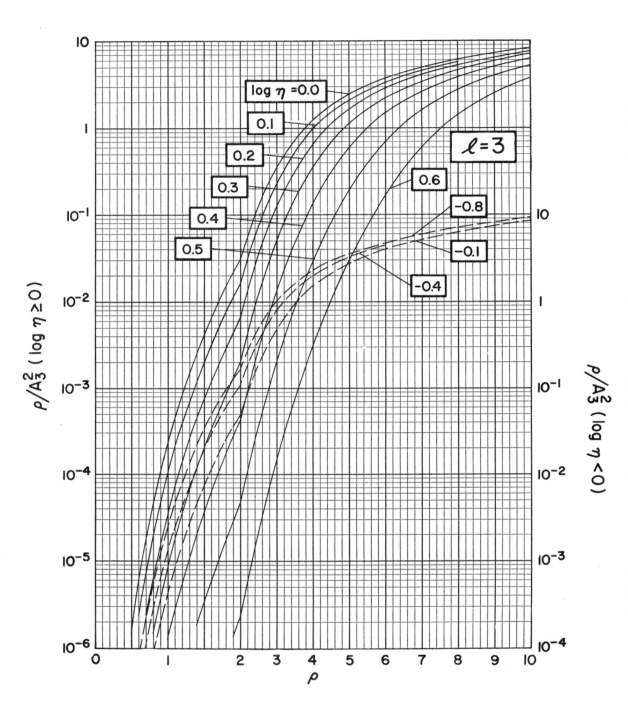

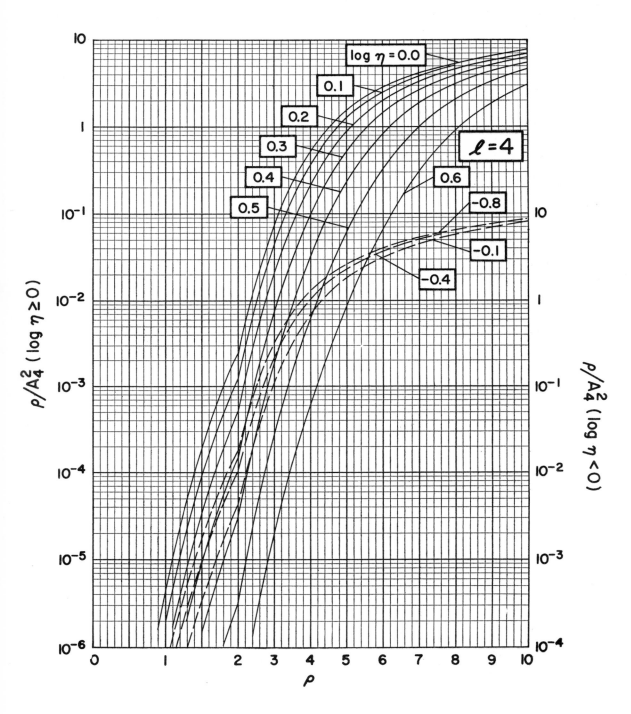

Figure 61. Penetrability functions for neutrons

The accompanying graph gives the neutron penetrability functions ϱ/A_l^2 for $l=0$ through $l=4$ as functions of ϱ. Equation (56.2) gives the appropriate relationship between the partial width, the penetrability, the shift function, and the reduced width, although the A_l^2 used here is not, of course, defined in terms of F_l and G_l.

The neutron penetrabilities, $P_l = \varrho/A_l^2$, were calculated from the following expressions:[1,2]

$$P_0(\varrho) = \varrho \tag{61.1}$$

$$P_1(\varrho) = \varrho^3(1+\varrho^2)^{-1} \tag{61.2}$$

$$P_2(\varrho) = \varrho^5(9+3\varrho^2+\varrho^4)^{-1} \tag{61.3}$$

$$P_3(\varrho) = \varrho^7(225+45\varrho^2+6\varrho^4+\varrho^6)^{-1} \tag{61.4}$$

$$P_4(\varrho) = \varrho^9(11025+1575\varrho^2+135\varrho^4+10\varrho^6+\varrho^8)^{-1}. \tag{61.5}$$

[1] J. E. Monahan, L. C. Biedenharn and J. P. Schiffer, Tables of Neutron Penetrabilities and Shift Functions, Argonne National Laboratory Report ANL-5846, unpublished (1958).

[2] H. B. Willard, L. C. Biedenharn, P. Huber and E. Baumgartner, in Fast Neutron Physics, eds. J. B. Marion and J. L. Fowler, Part II (Wiley-Interscience, New York, 1963) p. 1217.

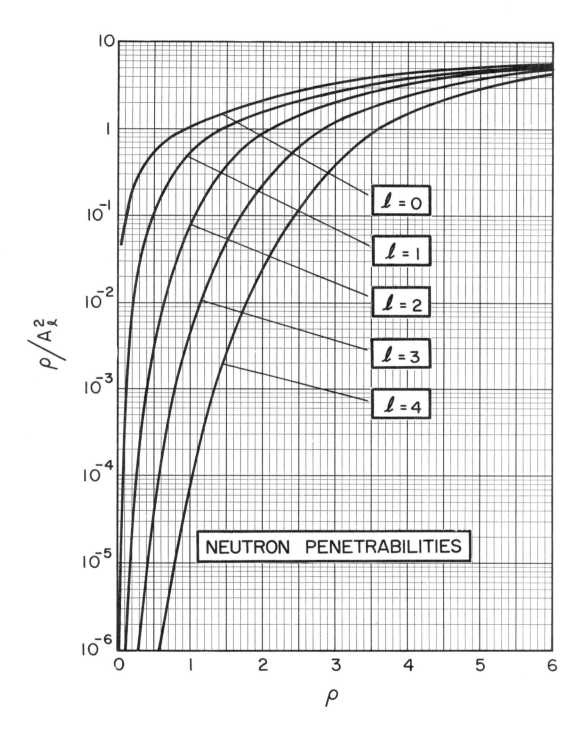

NEUTRON PENETRABILITIES

93

Figure 62. *Shift functions for neutrons*

The accompanying graph gives the neutron shift functions, S_L, for $L=0$ through $L=6$ as functions of ϱ. The neutron shift functions for both positive- and negative-energy channels were plotted from the values listed in reference 1. The definition of the shift function for positive-energy channels is given by eq. (56.3). The expression which applies for negative-energy channels is given in reference 1.

[1] J. E. Monahan, L. C. Biedenharn and J. P. Schiffer, Tables of Neutron Penetrabilities and Shift Functions, Argonne National Laboratory Report ANL-5846, unpublished (1958).

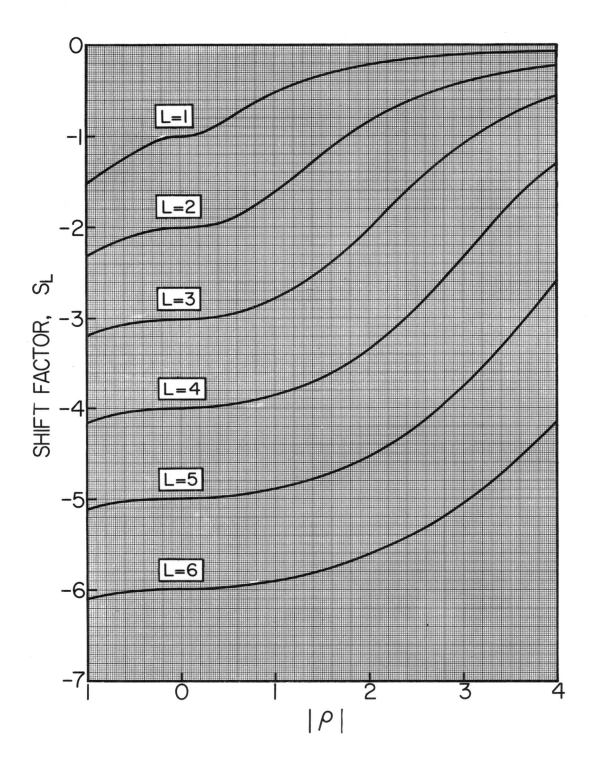

V. *Radiology and Shielding*

97

Figure 63.   Variation with γ-ray energy of the dose rate at 1 m *for a* 1-mC *source*

The accompanying graph shows the dose rate (in mr/mC-hr) at a distance of 1 m from a point source. It is assumed that there is no absorption in the intervening medium (approximately true for air).

This figure is taken from Slack and Way,[1] where a brief summary of γ-ray dose rate calculations is given.

[1] L. Slack and K. Way, *Radiations from Radioactive Atoms*, U.S. Government Printing Office (February 1959).

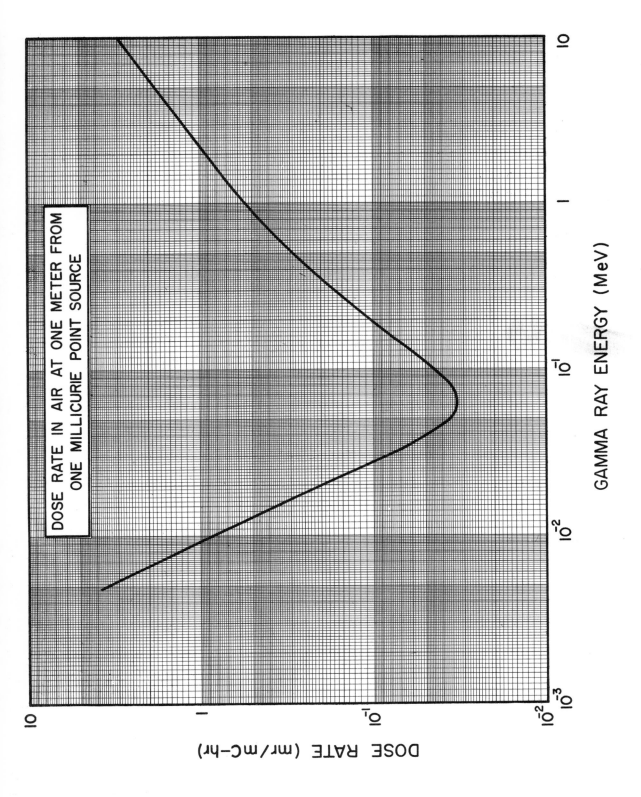

DOSE RATE IN AIR AT ONE METER FROM ONE MILLICURIE POINT SOURCE

GAMMA RAY ENERGY (MeV)

DOSE RATE (mr/mC-hr)

Figure 64.   Half-value thickness for γ rays in lead and concrete

The opposite curves, taken from Slack and Way,[1] give the thickness (in cm) of lead or concrete necessary to reduce by a factor of two the number of quanta, with the initial energy, in a broad beam of monoenergetic photons. The calculations were based on attenuation coefficients which were the sum of the coefficients for incoherent Compton scattering, the photoelectric effect, and pair production. The density of lead was assumed to be 11.29 g/cm^3. The density of concrete was assumed to be 2.35 g/cm^3.

[1] L. Slack and K. Way, *Radiations from Radioactive Atoms*, U.S. Government Printing Office (February 1959).

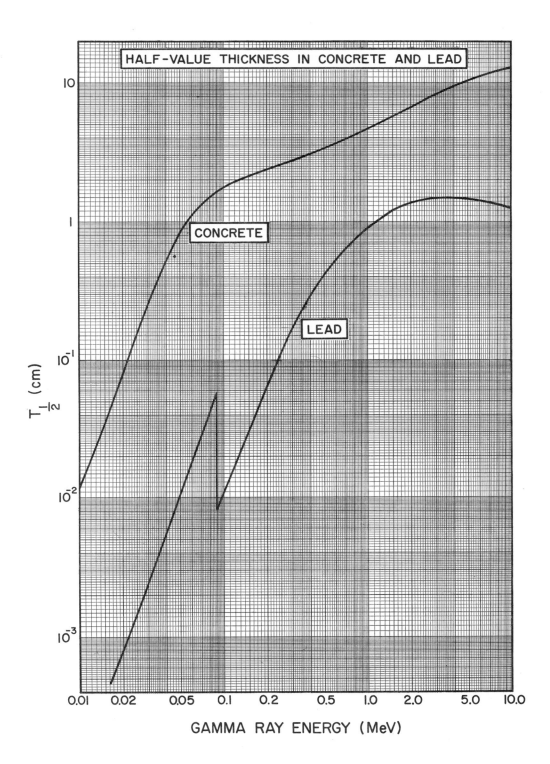

101

Figure 65.   Half-value thickness for neutrons in concrete

The accompanying graph shows the thickness of ordinary concrete (density $=2.4$ g/cm^3) that is necessary to attenuate neutrons to one-half of the incident number. The curve is that drawn by Wallace[1] through several measured and calculated points.

[1] R. Wallace, Nuclear Instr. and Meth. *18/19* (1962) 405; see also "Conference on Shielding of High Energy Accelerators," U.S. Atomic Energy Commission Report TID-7545, unpublished (1957).

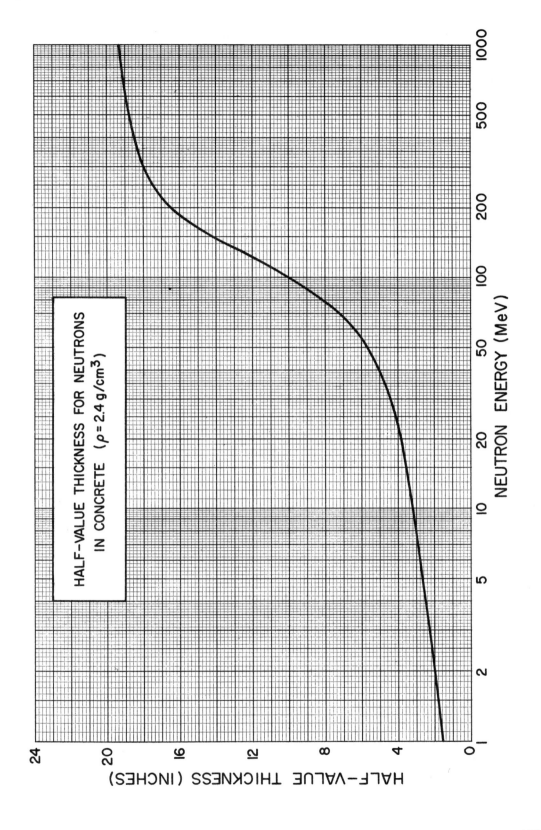

HALF-VALUE THICKNESS FOR NEUTRONS
IN CONCRETE ($\rho = 2.4$ g/cm^3)

HALF-VALUE THICKNESS (INCHES)

24 20 16 12 8 4 0

NEUTRON ENERGY (MeV)

1 2 5 10 20 50 100 200 500 1000

103

Figure 66.   Neutron attenuation in concrete and water

The graph opposite gives the attenuation of neutrons in concrete and water at energies of 1 and 6 MeV. (The attenuation of fission neutrons can be obtained from the curves for 6-MeV neutrons.) The concrete is of density 2.3 g/cm^3 (4 parts limestone gravel, 2 parts sand, 1 part Portland cement; cured). The intensity unit refers to the decrease in relative dose rate for an incident parallel beam of neutrons, although the intensity unit can be considered as approximately equivalent to neutron flux as well. The curves take into account the build up of neutrons of lower energy as the fast neutrons are moderated.

This figure is adapted from that given by Hughes and Harvey.[1]

[1] D. J. Hughes and J. A. Harvey, in *American Institute of Physics Handbook*, ed. D. E. Gray (McGraw-Hill, New York, 1957) p. 8–169.

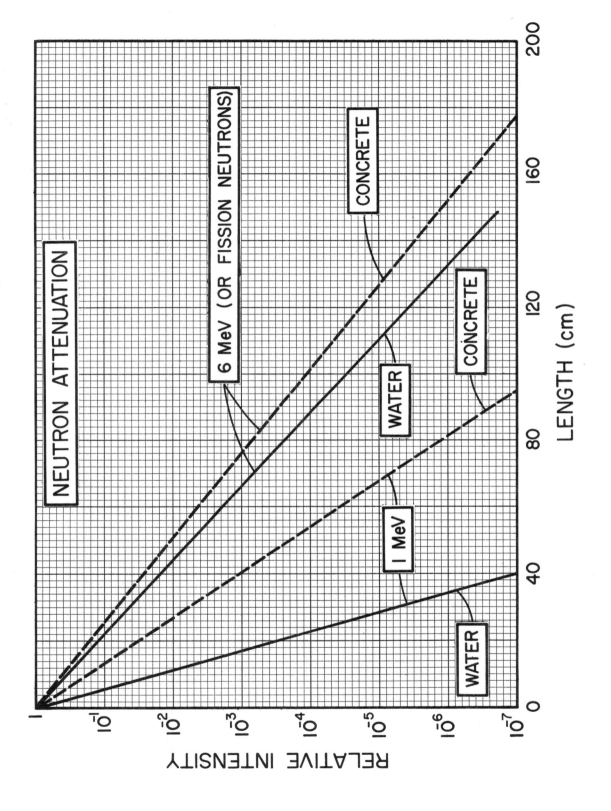

VI. *Miscellaneous*

Figure 67.   Coulomb barrier heights for protons and α particles

The height of the Coulomb barrier of a nucleus of charge $Z_1 e$ and radius R_1 for a particle of charge $Z_2 e$ is given by

$$E_C = Z_1 Z_2 e^2/(R_1 + R_2).$$ (67.1)

A common expression for the interaction radius is:

$$R = R_1 + R_2 = R_0(A_1^{\frac{1}{3}} + A_2^{\frac{1}{3}})$$ (67.2)

where A_1 and A_2 are the mass numbers of the nucleus and the particle, respectively.

The accompanying graph shows the Coulomb barrier heights for protons and α particles calculated with the above equations for R_0 equal to 1.0, 1.2, and 1.4 fm. The curves are plotted as functions of Z_1 and were drawn smoothly through points calculated for the most abundant isotopes of given (A_1, Z_1) values.

The solid curves are for protons and the dashed curves are for α particles.

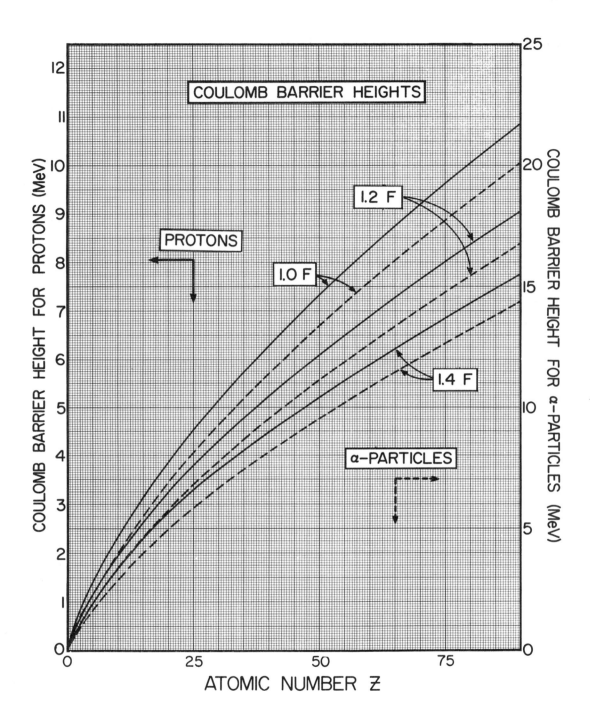

COULOMB BARRIER HEIGHTS

Figure 68. Bϱ-values for charged particles

The accompanying graph shows $B\varrho$-values for the charged particles commonly analyzed by magnetic methods: protons, deuterons, tritons, He^3 ions, and He^4 ions.

The most general (relativistic) expression for the kinetic energy E of a particle of rest mass M_0 and charge Ze in a magnetic field B is

$$\frac{E}{M_0 c^2} + 1 = (\eta^2 + 1)^{\frac{1}{2}} \tag{68.1}$$

where

$$\eta = \frac{Ze}{M_0 c^2} B\varrho \tag{68.2}$$

$$= 3.2184594 \times 10^{-7}(Z/M)B\varrho \quad \text{(in cgs units)} \tag{68.3}$$

so that

$$B\varrho = 3.107077 \times 10^6 \left(\frac{M}{Z}\right) \left[\left(\frac{E}{M_0 c^2}\right)^2 + \frac{2E}{M_0 c^2}\right]^{\frac{1}{2}}. \tag{68.4}$$

The quantity M in the above equations is the mass of the particle in amu, and the numerical factors are based on the 1964 adjustment of the fundamental physical constants;[1] $B\varrho$ is the magnetic rigidity in gauss-cm.

For small η, eq. (68.1) may be expanded as follows:

$$E = M_0 c^2 (\tfrac{1}{2}\eta^2 - \tfrac{1}{8}\eta^4 + \tfrac{1}{16}\eta^6 - \ldots)$$

$$= a(B\varrho)^2 + b(B\varrho)^4 + c(B\varrho)^6. \tag{68.5}$$

The constants a, b, c for hydrogen and helium ions are given below. (Note that b is negative.)

Ion	a in 10^{-12} keV(G-cm)$^{-2}$	$-b$ in 10^{-24} keV(G-cm)$^{-4}$	c in 10^{-36} keV(G-cm)$^{-6}$
H^+	47894.96	1222.441	62.399
D^+	23959.30	153.032	1.955
T^+	15998.54	45.5613	0.2595
He^{3+}	15998.57	45.5622	0.2595
He^{3++}	64006.07	729.3945	16.625
He^{4+}	12054.71	19.4907	0.06303
He^{4++}	48225.33	311.978	4.037

[1] E. R. Cohen and J. W. M. DuMond, Revs. Modern Phys. 37 (1965) 537.

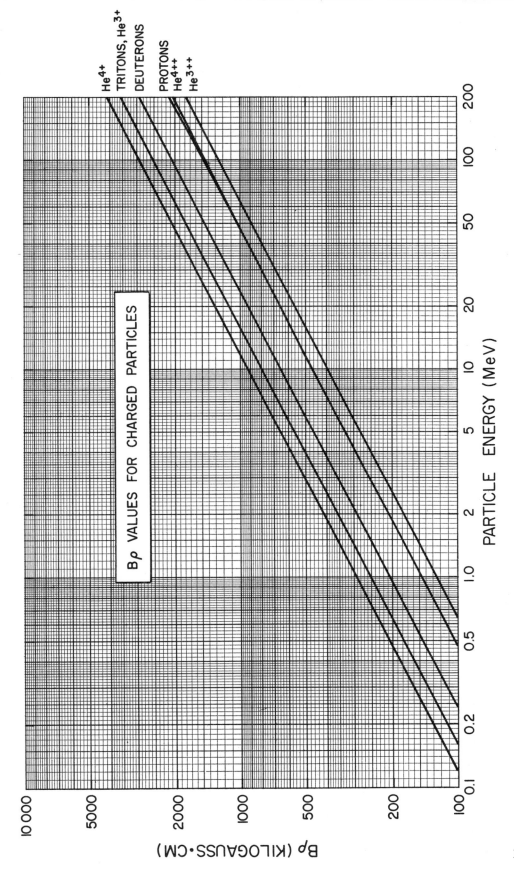

Bρ VALUES FOR CHARGED PARTICLES

He^{4+}
TRITONS, He^{3+}
DEUTERONS
PROTONS
He^{4++}
He^{3++}

PARTICLE ENERGY (MeV)

Bρ (KILOGAUSS·CM)

111

Figure 69. Target thickness effects on resonance widths and yields

The apparent width of a resonance in a nuclear reaction and the yield of particles or γ rays from that resonance are influenced by the thickness of the target employed in the experiment.[1] If it is valid to assume that the stopping cross section ε of the material and the energy loss ξ of the particle beam in the target are independent of the beam energy E in the vicinity of the resonance, then the yield is given by:

$$Y = \varepsilon^{-1} \int_{E-\xi}^{E} \sigma(E) \mathrm{d}E .$$ (69.1)

ξ and ε are related by $\xi = Nt\varepsilon$, where N is the number of disintegrable nuclei/cm^3 in the target and t is the target thickness in cm; Nt is then the areal density (number of atoms/cm^2). If σ follows the Breit–Wigner relation, then

$$Y = \frac{\sigma_R \Gamma}{2\varepsilon} \left[\tan^{-1}\left(\frac{E-E_R}{\frac{1}{2}\Gamma}\right) - \tan^{-1}\left(\frac{E-E_R-\xi}{\frac{1}{2}\Gamma}\right) \right]$$ (69.2)

where $\sigma_R = \sigma(E_R)$. For a given ξ, eq. (69.2) has a maximum at $E = E_R + \frac{1}{2}\xi$ given by

$$Y_{max}(\xi) = (\sigma_R \Gamma / \varepsilon) \tan^{-1}(\xi/\Gamma) .$$ (69.3)

For an 'infinitely thick' target the maximum yield or 'thick target step' is given by:

$$Y_{max}(\infty) = \tfrac{1}{2}\pi\sigma_R \Gamma / \varepsilon .$$ (69.4)

Therefore,

$$Y_{max}(\xi) / Y_{max}(\infty) = (2/\pi) \tan^{-1}(\xi/\Gamma) .$$ (69.5)

This ratio is shown in the accompanying graph together with the ratio of the observed width Γ' to the natural width Γ of the resonance:

$$\Gamma' = (\Gamma^2 + \xi^2)^{\frac{1}{2}}$$ (69.6)

or

$$\Gamma'/\Gamma = [1 + (\xi/\Gamma)^2]^{\frac{1}{2}} .$$ (69.7)

[1] W. A. Fowler, C. C. Lauritsen and T. Lauritsen, Revs. Modern Phys. 20 (1948) 236.

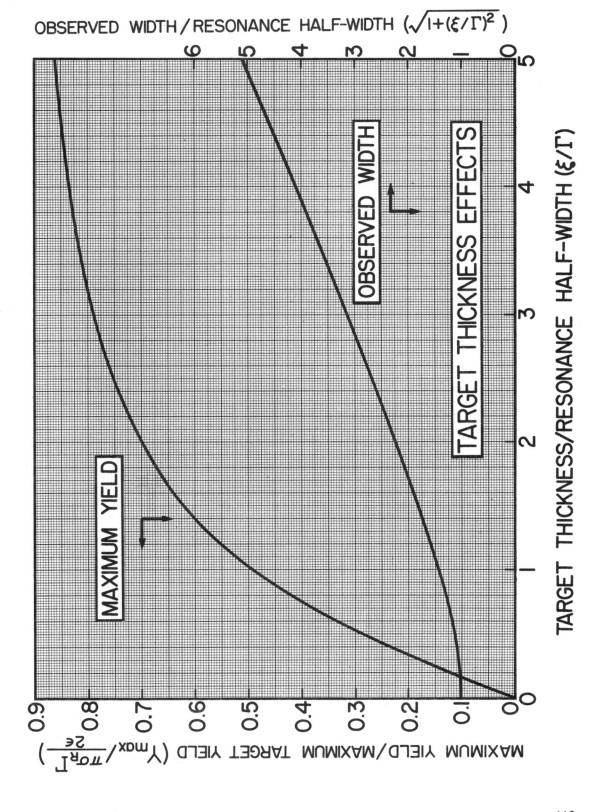

113

Figure 70.   *Average ionic charge in a helium beam*

Helium ions are frequently used as the incident beam in studying nuclear reactions. It is important to know the average ionic charge in a helium beam which is in charge equilibrium for purposes of current integration. The average ionic charge $\bar{Q}$ is related to the charge-state fractions, ϕ_i (see Fig. 24) by the equation

$$\bar{Q} = \phi_1 + 2\phi_2 . \tag{70.1}$$

By using this relationship, the value of $\bar{Q}$ as a function of energy was computed from the measurements of Armstrong et al.[1] and is shown in the accompanying graph. In order to facilitate accurate reading of the values of $\bar{Q}$ near 2, a curve of the quantity $(2 - \bar{Q}) \times 10$ is also plotted. The same ordinate serves for both curves.

[1] J. C. Armstrong, J. V. Mullendore, W. R. Harris and J. B. Marion, Proc. Phys. Soc. (London) 86 (1965) 1283.

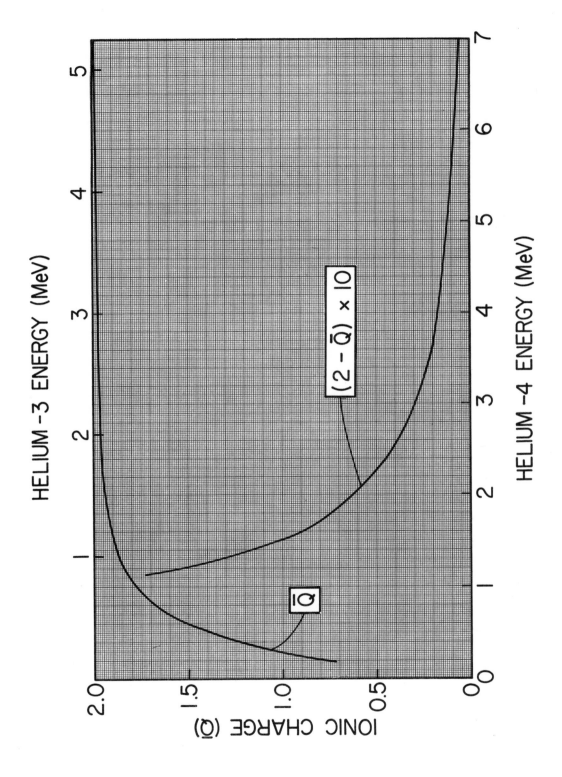

Figure 71. *Allowable beam currents of protons and deuterons on thin nickel foils*

Thin nickel foils are frequently used as entrance windows for gas target cells. The energy loss in the foil of the charged-particle beam entering the target can rupture the foil if the average beam current is too large. The data[1] presented in the graph opposite apply for thin (0.05–0.10 mil) nickel foils mounted over a $\frac{3}{16}''$ diam. hole and bombarded by a $\frac{1}{10}''$ diam. beam. Estimates of the performance of foils under different conditions may be made based on the fact that the dominant process of heat transfer from the foil is by lateral conduction through the foil to its mounting block.[1] Therefore the maximum beam current which a foil can withstand is inversely proportional to its stopping cross section.

[1] J. H. Coon, in *Fast Neutron Physics*, eds. J. B. Marion and J. L. Fowler, Part I (Wiley-Interscience, New York, 1960) p. 677.

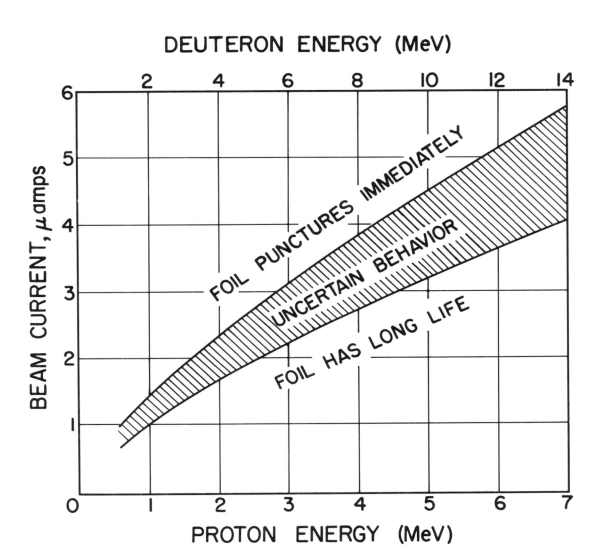

DEUTERON ENERGY (MeV)

BEAM CURRENT, μ amps

FOIL PUNCTURES IMMEDIATELY

UNCERTAIN BEHAVIOR

FOIL HAS LONG LIFE

PROTON ENERGY (MeV)

Figures 72–74. Energies of elastically scattered particles

In the study of angular distributions of elastically scattered particles or in the measurement of the energies of reaction products it is frequently necessary to know the energy of the elastically scattered particles as a function of the scattering angle. The ratio of the energy of the scattered particle E_1 to the incident energy E_0 is given in the non-relativistic limit by:

$$\frac{E_1}{E_0} = \frac{2\cos^2\psi + R^2 - 1 + 2\cos\psi\sqrt{\cos^2\psi + R^2 - 1}}{(1+R)^2} \tag{72.1}$$

where ψ is the laboratory scattering angle and where $R = M_2/M_1$ is the ratio of the mass of the target nucleus to the mass of the incident particle.

The accompanying graph shows E_1/E_0 as a function of R for $\psi = 30°, 60°, 90°, 120°, 150°$, and $180°$. The two graphs following show E_1/E_0 as a function of ψ for 20 values of R which were chosen to correspond to situations frequently encountered (e.g., protons on oxygen and gold, deuterons on carbon, etc.).

For further equations relating to reaction kinematics, see Table 5, page 140. Tables are also available[1] which facilitate the calculation of the energies of reaction products as functions of laboratory angle.

---

[1] J. B. Marion, T. I. Arnette and H. C. Owens, Tables for the Transformation between the Laboratory and Center-of-Mass Coordinate Systems and for the Calculation of the Energies of Reaction Products, Oak Ridge National Laboratory Report ORNL-2574, unpublished (1959).

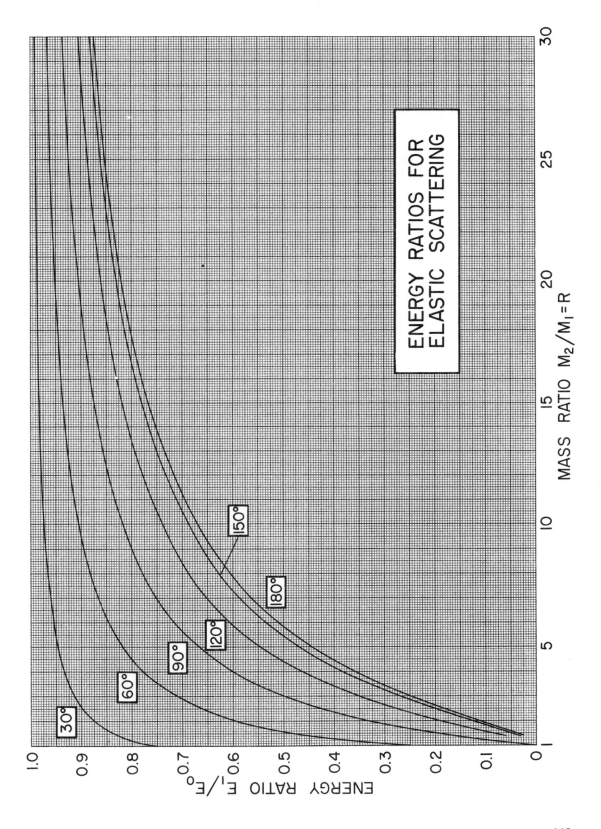

ENERGY RATIOS FOR
ELASTIC SCATTERING

MASS RATIO $M_2/M_1 = R$

ENERGY RATIO E_1/E_0

119

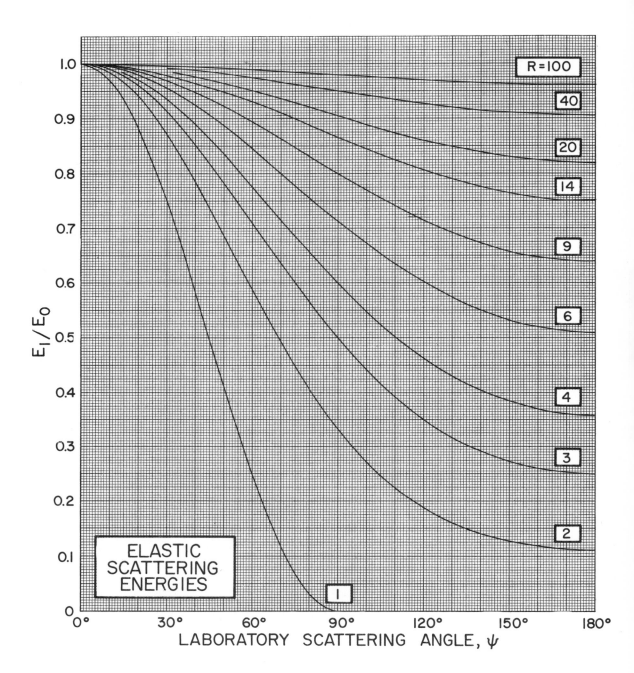

ELASTIC
SCATTERING
ENERGIES

120

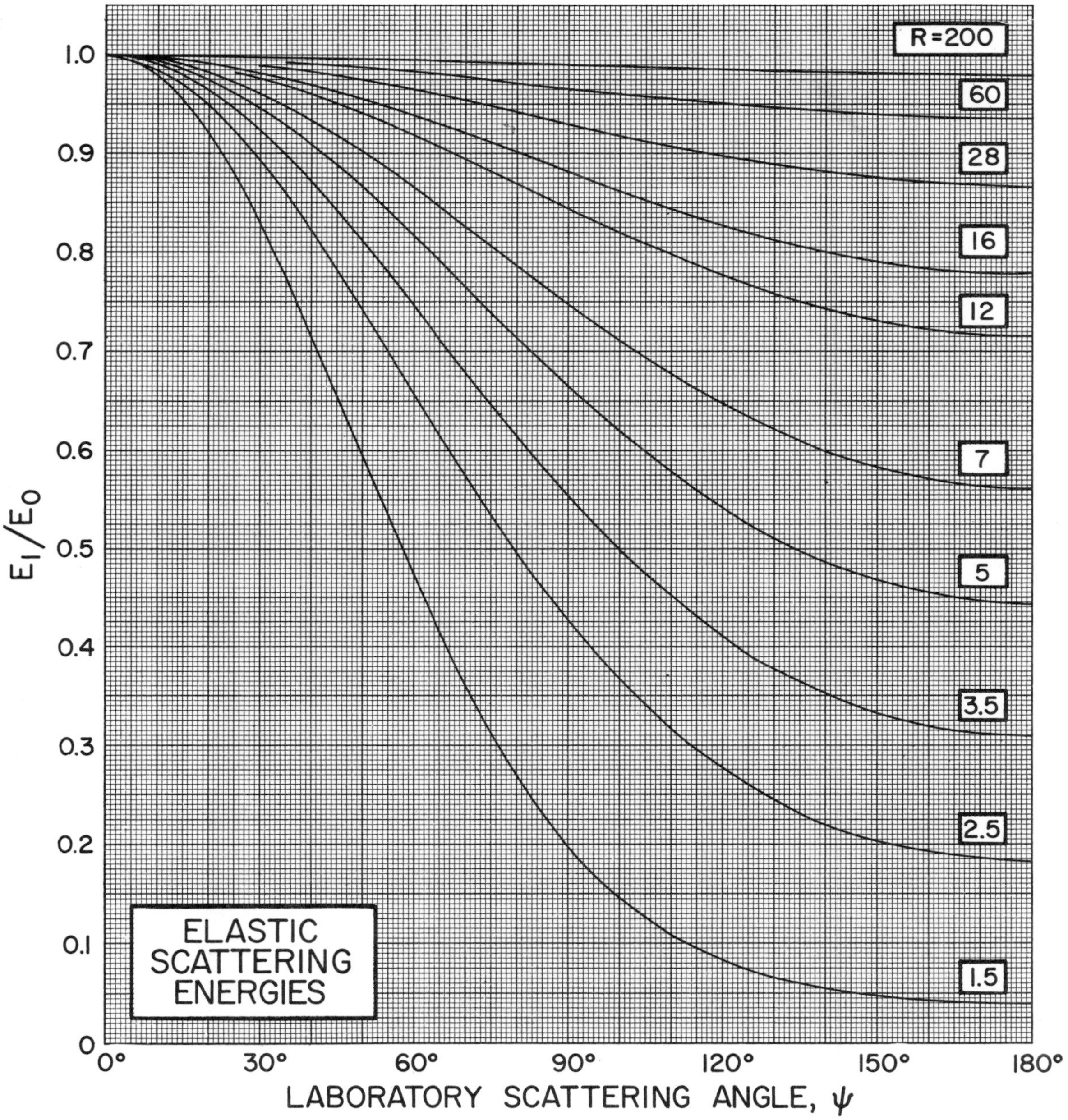
R=200
60
28
16
12
7
5
3.5
2.5
1.5
1.0
0.9
0.8
0.7
0.6
0.5
0.4
0.3
0.2
0.1
0
E1/E0
ELASTIC SCATTERING ENERGIES
0°
30°
60°
90°
120°
150°
180°
LABORATORY SCATTERING ANGLE, ψ

Figure 75.   Neutron total cross sections for hydrogen and helium

The accompanying curves show the n–p and n–He total cross sections for neutron energies $0.01 \lesssim E_{n,lab} \lesssim 100$ MeV.

The n–p total cross section curve for $0.1 \leq E_n \leq 35$ MeV is based on Gammel's phenomenological formula:[1]

$$\sigma_T(E) = 3\pi[1.206E + (-1.860 + 0.0941491E + 0.000130658E^2)E^2]^{-1} + \pi[1.206E + (0.4223 + 0.1300E)^2]^{-1} \tag{75.1}$$

where σ_T is in barns and E is in MeV (lab). Equation (75.1) duplicates to within an average deviation of less than 0.2 per cent all of the precision n–p total cross section measurements in the energy range considered. For $E_n < 0.1$ MeV and $E_n > 35$ MeV, the curve is from BNL-325.[2]

A useful approximation for the n–p total cross section which is accurate to within about 3 per cent for $0.3 < E < 30$ MeV is:

$$\sigma_T(E) \cong 4.83[E(\text{MeV})]^{-\frac{1}{2}} - 0.578 \text{ barns} . \tag{75.2}$$

Since the angular distribution in n–p scattering is isotropic in the center-of-mass system for incident neutron energies below about 10 MeV,[3] the total cross section may be used to compute the laboratory differential cross section at any angle ψ:

$$\sigma(\psi) = (\sigma_T \cos \psi)/\pi . \tag{75.3}$$

The energy of the scattered proton in the laboratory system may be computed from:

$$E_{p,lab} = E_{n,lab} \cos^2 \psi_p \tag{75.4}$$

where ψ_p is the laboratory angle at which the proton is scattered.

The n–p total cross section for lower energies (down to 0.1 keV) is shown in the following figure.

The solid portion of the n–He total cross section curve is taken from the Brookhaven summary graph.[4] The data points above 40 MeV are from Hillman et al.[5] and Measday and Palmieri.[6] The dashed curve merely connects the solid curve and the data points.

[1] J. L. Gammel, in *Fast Neutron Physics*, eds. J. B. Marion and J. L. Fowler, Part II (Wiley-Interscience, New York, 1963) p. 2185.

[2] D. J. Hughes and R. B. Schwartz, Neutron Cross Sections, Brookhaven National Laboratory Report BNL-325, 2nd ed., unpublished (1958).

[3] J. E. Perry, Jr., in *Fast Neutron Physics*, ed. J. B. Marion and J. L. Fowler, Part I (Wiley-Interscience, New York, 1960) p. 623.

[4] J. R. Stehn, M. D. Goldberg, B. A. Magurno and R. Wiener-Chasman, Neutron Cross Sections, Vol. 1, $Z = 1$ to 20, Brookhaven National Laboratory Report BNL-325, 2nd ed., Suppl. no. 2, unpublished (1964).

[5] P. Hillman, R. H. Stahl and N. F. Ramsey, Phys. Rev. 96 (1954) 115.

[6] D. F. Measday and J. N. Palmieri, Nuclear Phys. 85 (1966) 129.

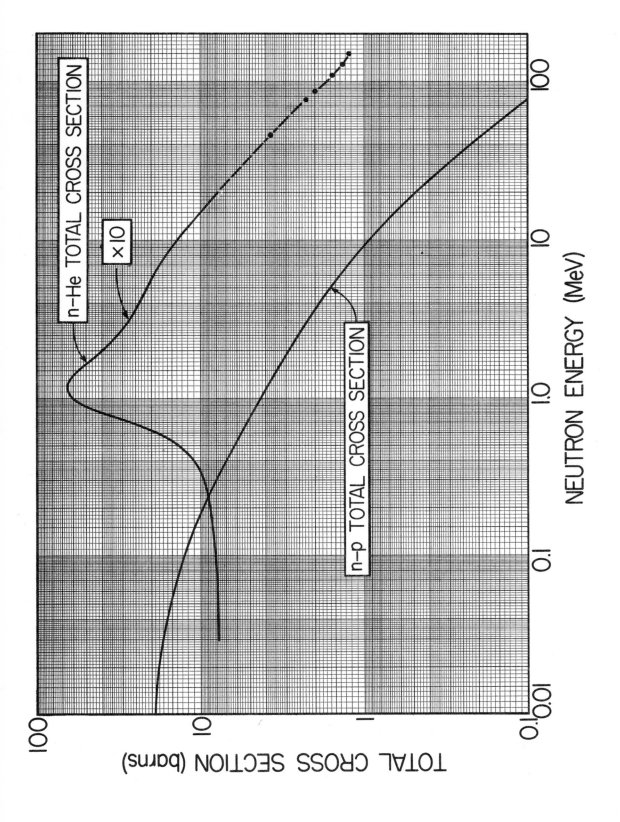

NEUTRON ENERGY (MeV)

TOTAL CROSS SECTION (barns)

n-He TOTAL CROSS SECTION

×10

n-p TOTAL CROSS SECTION

123

Figure 76.   Cross sections for the $H(n,n)H$, $He^3(n,p)T$, $Li^6(n,\alpha)T$, *and* $B^{10}(n,\alpha)Li^7$ *reactions*

The accompanying graph shows neutron cross section curves derived from the following sources:

$H(n,n)H$: $100 < E_n < 10\,000$ keV, Gammel's formula[1] (see previous figure).
$E_n < 100$ keV, BNL-325[2] (the two curves shown in this reference were joined smoothly in the region $2 < E_n < 10$ keV).

$He^3(n,p)T$: $10 < E_n < 10\,000$ keV, BNL-325.[3]
$E_n < 10$ keV, $\sigma \propto E_n^{-\frac{1}{2}}$.

$Li^6(n,\alpha)T$: $10 < E_n < 10\,000$ keV, BNL-325.[3]
$E_n < 10$ keV, $\sigma \propto E_n^{-\frac{1}{2}}$.
Significant disagreements in measured $Li^6(n,\alpha)T$ cross sections (40% at 400 keV, for example) have been recently reviewed.[4]

$B^{10}(n,\alpha)Li^7$:   The curve given is for $\sigma(n,\alpha_0) + \sigma(n,\alpha_1)$.
$200 < E_n < 7\,600$ keV, BNL-325.[3]
$E_n < 100$ keV, $\sigma \propto E_n^{-\frac{1}{2}}$, normalized to $\sigma_{thermal} = 3840$ barns, BNL-325.[3] These two regions were then joined smoothly.

[1] J. L. Gammel, in *Fast Neutron Physics*, eds. J. B. Marion and J. L. Fowler, Part II (Wiley-Interscience, New York, 1963) p. 2185.
[2] D. J. Hughes and R. B. Schwartz, Neutron Cross Sections, Brookhaven National Laboratory Report BNL-325, 2nd ed., unpublished (1958).
[3] J. R. Stehn, M. D. Goldberg, B. A. Magurno and R. Wiener-Chasman, Neutron Cross Sections, Vol. 1, $Z = 1$ to 20, Brookhaven National Laboratory Report BNL-325, 2nd ed., Suppl. no. 2, unpublished (1964).
[4] A. Bergström, S. Schwarz, L. G. Strömberg and L. Wallin, Remarks on the $^6Li(n,\alpha)^3H$ Cross Section in the Region $1 < E_n < 600$ keV, Newsletter No. 3, p. 7, Neutron Data Compilation Centre Report CCDN-NW3, European Nuclear Energy Agency, unpublished (1966).

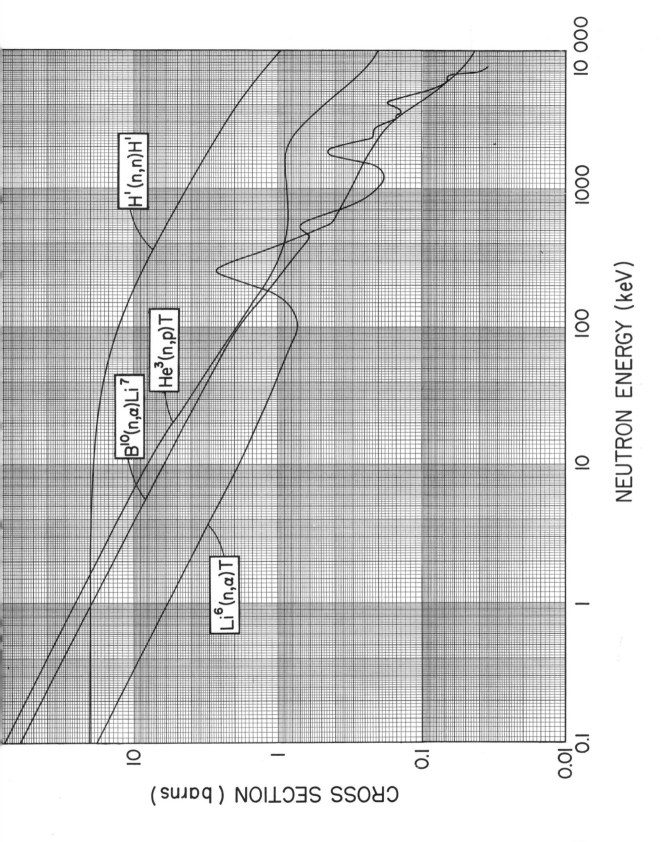

CROSS SECTION (barns)

NEUTRON ENERGY (keV)

$H^1(n,n)H^1$

$He^3(n,p)T$

$B^{10}(n,\alpha)Li^7$

$Li^6(n,\alpha)T$

125

Figure 77.   Efficiency of long counters

The flat-response long counter[1] is often used both as a neutron monitor and to measure the neutron flux from reactions. The efficiency curve or response function of such a counter is not absolutely flat and corrections for this effect are sometimes needed. Both the decrease of the n–p scattering cross section with increasing neutron energy and the occurrences of resonances in the neutron scattering cross section of carbon contribute to the energy dependence of the efficiency. The relative efficiency can be computed from the following expression:

$$\text{Efficiency ratio} = 0.3206f - 0.02167E_n + 0.8406 \qquad (77.1)$$

where E_n is in MeV and

$$f = 2\sigma_H/(\sigma_C + 2\sigma_H) ; \qquad (77.2)$$

σ_H and σ_C are the neutron total cross sections for hydrogen and carbon, respectively. This efficiency expression is shown in the accompanying graph. The empirical response function for a long counter has been shown[2] to agree closely (r.m.s. difference $= 1.5$ per cent) to the calculated curve.

It must be emphasized that differences in long counter construction will alter the efficiency curve and that the curve given here will therefore only be approximately correct for other long counters. It should, however, still provide a useful approximation to the efficiency for most long counters.

[1] A. O. Hanson and J. L. McKibben, Phys. Rev. 72 (1947) 673.

[2] G. Haddad, R. L. Henkel, J. E. Perry, Jr. and R. K. Smith, unpublished results (1958).

[3] See, for example, W. D. Allen, in Fast Neutron Physics, eds. J. B. Marion and J. L. Fowler, Part I (Wiley-Interscience, New York, 1960) p. 361.

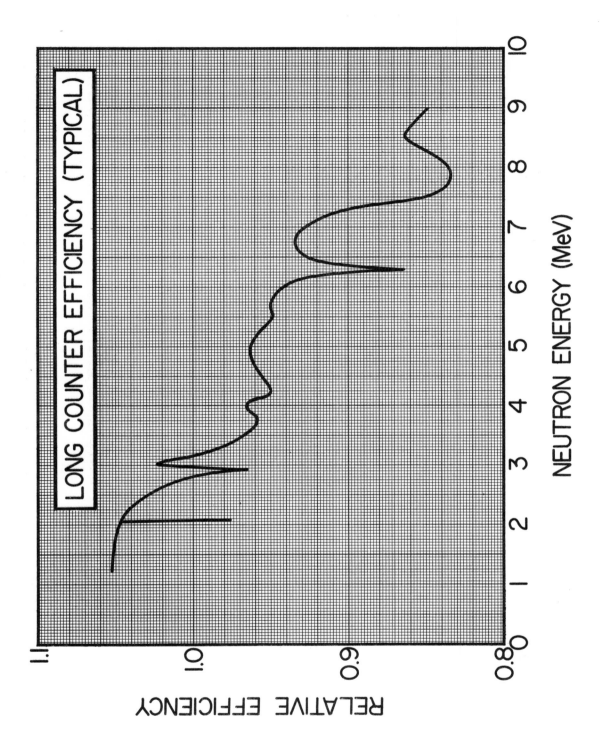

LONG COUNTER EFFICIENCY (TYPICAL)

NEUTRON ENERGY (MeV)

RELATIVE EFFICIENCY

127

Figure 78.   *Surface-barrier silicon detector nomograph*

The use of surface-barrier silicon counters is now standard in many phases of nuclear particle detection. The accompanying nomograph, prepared by Blankenship and Borkowski[1] permits the determination of the parameters of these counters for particular cases of particle detection. The dotted line extending across the diagram relates to the following example: If p-type silicon which has a resistivity of 9500 Ω-cm is used, and if a bias voltage of 46 V is applied to the diode, then the barrier layer will be approximately 205 μm deep and protons of 5.0 MeV will come to rest within the barrier layer and the full energy release will be available for the output signal.

[1] J. L. Blankenship and C. J. Borkowski, Proc. IRE, *NS*-7 (1960) 190. The nomograph is ORNL Drawing No. 45902.

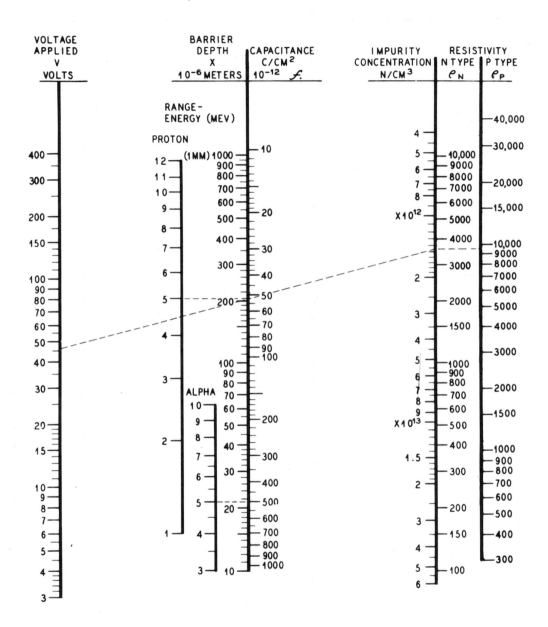

VOLTAGE
APPLIED
V
VOLTS

BARRIER
DEPTH
X
10⁻⁶ METERS

CAPACITANCE
C/CM²
10⁻¹² $f.$

IMPURITY
CONCENTRATION
N/CM³

RESISTIVITY
N TYPE   P TYPE
ρ_N ρ_P

RANGE-
ENERGY (MEV)

PROTON

ALPHA

129

Figures 79, 80.   Values of log ft for beta decay

The nomogram on the page opposite (Fig. 80) and the graph below (Fig. 79) allow the determination of log ft values for $\beta^{\pm}$ decay. Such a nomogram was originally constructed by Moszkowski;[1] the extended version shown here was prepared by Verrall et al.[2]

The log ft value for a transition is given by

$$\log ft = \log f_0 t + \log C \tag{79.1}$$

where $\log f_0 t$ is obtained from the nomogram and where C is the Coulomb correction factor and can be read (or interpolated) from the graph below. The log C calculations contain an approximate correction for the screening effect of atomic electrons. The effect of the finite size of the nucleus has not been taken into account. The calculations of Rose and Holmes[3] show that for $Z < 60$ the correction is negligible. For $Z = 60$, log C should be lowered by about 0.01 and for $Z = 96$, log C should be lowered by about 0.09. This correction is almost independent of energy.

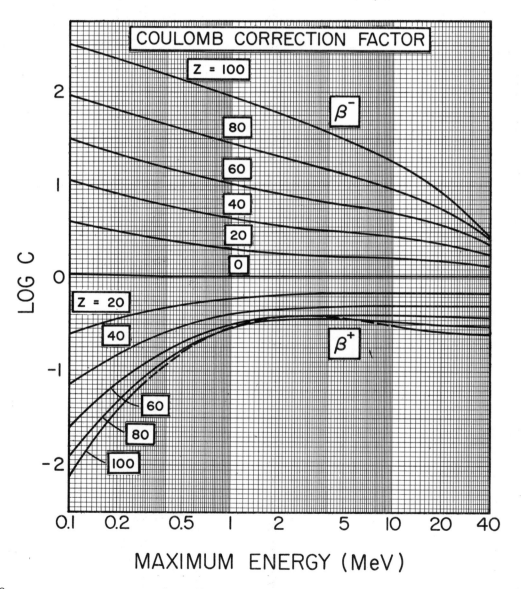

Empirically, it is found that log *ft* values can be divided into the following groups:

ΔJ	Parity change	Type	log *ft*
0	no	supperallowed	3.5 ± 0.5
0, 1	no ($\Delta l = 0$)	allowed	5 ± 1
	($\Delta l = 2$)	*l*-forbidden	may be > 6
0, 1	yes	1st forbidden	7 ± 1
2	yes	unique 1st forbidden	8.5 ± 0.5
2, 3	no	2nd forbidden	≈ 13
3, 4	yes	3rd forbidden	≈ 18

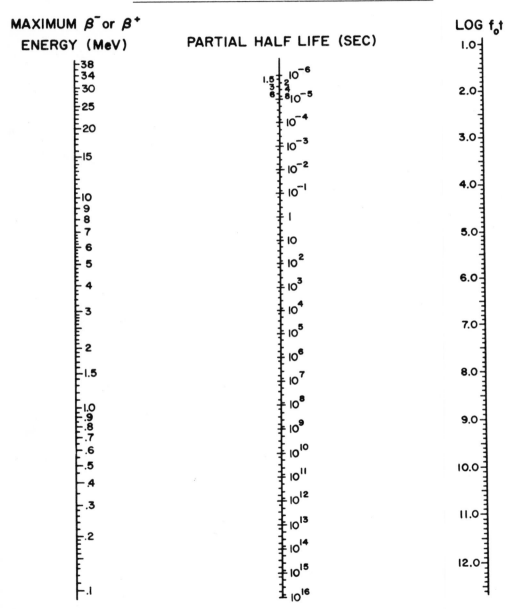

[1] S. A. Moszkowski, Phys. Rev. *82* (1951) 35.
[2] R. I. Verrall, J. C. Hardy and R. E. Bell, Nuclear Instr. and Meth. *42* (1966) 258.
[3] M. E. Rose and D. K. Holmes, Phys. Rev. *83* (1951) 190.

B. TABLES

TABLE 1

Physical properties of the elements

Atomic number	Element	Atomic or molecular weight	Density (g/cm^3)	Nuclei/cm^3 $(\times 10^{22})$
1	H_2	2.016	8.99×10^{-5}	**
2	He	4.003	17.85×10^{-5}	*
3	Li	6.940	0.534	4.64
4	Be	9.013	1.85	12.37
5	B	10.82	2.34^a	13.03
6	C	12.01	2.25^b	11.29
7	N_2	28.02	1.25×10^{-3}	**
8	O_2	32.000	1.43×10^{-3}	**
9	F_2	38.00	1.69×10^{-3}	**
10	Ne	20.18	9.00×10^{-4}	*
11	Na	22.99	0.97	2.54
12	Mg	24.32	1.74	4.31
13	Al	26.98	2.702	6.03
14	Si	28.09	2.329^a	5.19
15	P	30.98	1.82^c	3.54
16	S	32.066	2.07^d	3.89
17	Cl_2	70.91	3.214×10^{-3}	**
18	Ar	39.944	1.784×10^{-3}	*
19	K	39.10	0.86	1.33
20	Ca	40.08	1.55	2.33
21	Sc	44.96	2.5	3.35
22	Ti	47.90	4.5	5.66
23	V	50.95	5.96	7.05
24	Cr	52.01	7.20	8.34
25	Mn	54.94	7.20	7.90
26	Fe	55.85	7.86	8.48
27	Co	58.94	8.9	9.10
28	Ni	58.71	8.90	9.13
29	Cu	63.54	8.92	8.46
30	Zn	65.38	7.14	6.58
31	Ga	69.72	5.904^e	5.10
32	Ge	72.60	5.35^f	4.44
33	As	74.91	5.727^g	4.61
34	Se	78.96	4.82^h	3.68
35	Br_2	159.83	2.928	2.07
36	Kr	83.80	3.71×10^{-3}	*
37	Rb	85.48	1.532	1.08
38	Sr	87.63	2.6	1.79
39	Y	88.92	5.51	3.73
40	Zr	91.22	6.4	4.23
41	Nb	92.91	8.55	5.54
42	Mo	95.95	10.2	6.40
43	Tc	98	—	—
44	Ru	101.1	12.06^i	7.19
45	Rh	102.91	12.4	7.26

   * Monatomic gas: 2.69×10^{19} nuclei/cm^3 at NTP
 ** Diatomic gas: 5.38×10^{19} nuclei/cm^3 at NTP
 [a] Single crystal
 [b] Graphite
 [c] Yellow phosphorus, P_4; mol. wt = 123.92
 [d] Rhombic, S_8; mol. wt = 256.53
 [e] Solid. 29.6°C; melting point = 29.8°C
 [f] 5.325 at 77°K
 [g] Black crystal, As_4; mol. wt = 299.64
 [h] Amorphous, Se_8; mol. wt = 631.68
 [i] Hexagonal

TABLE 1

Physical properties of the elements (continued)

Atomic number	Element	Atomic or molecular weight	Density (g/cm^3)	Nuclei/cm^3 ($\times 10^{22}$)
46	Pd	106.70	11.40^j	6.44
47	Ag	107.88	10.5	5.86
48	Cd	112.41	8.642	4.63
49	In	114.82	7.30	3.83
50	Sn	118.70	7.28^k	3.70
51	Sb	121.76	6.684	3.07
52	Te$_2$	255.22	6.25	2.95
53	I$_2$	253.81	4.93	2.34
54	Xe	131.3	5.85×10^{-3}	*
55	Cs	132.91	1.873	0.85
56	Ba	137.36	3.5	1.54
57	La	138.92	6.15	2.67
58	Ce	140.13	6.7^i	2.88
59	Pr	140.92	6.5	2.78
60	Nd	144.27	6.9	2.88
61	Pm	145	—	—
62	Sm	150.35	7.7	3.09
63	Eu	152.00	5.22	2.07
64	Gd	157.26	7.95	3.05
65	Td	158.93	8.33	3.16
66	Dy	162.51	8.56	3.17
67	Ho	164.94	8.76	3.20
68	Er	167.20	9.16	3.30
69	Tm	168.94	9.35	3.33
70	Yb	173.04	7.01	2.44
71	Lu	174.99	9.74	3.35
72	Hf	178.60	13.3	4.49
73	Ta	180.95	16.6^l	5.53
74	W	183.86	19.3	6.32
75	Re	186.22	20.53	6.64
76	Os	190.20	22.48	7.12
77	Ir	192.2	22.42	7.03
78	Pt	195.09	21.45	6.62
79	Au	197.0	19.3	5.90
80	Hg	200.61	13.55	4.07
81	Tl	204.39	11.85	3.49
82	Pb	207.21	11.34	3.30
83	Bi	209.00	9.80	2.83
84	Po	210	9.24	2.65
85	At	211	—	—
86	Rn	222.00	9.73×10^{-3}	*
87	Fr	223	—	—
88	Ra	226.05	5	1.3
89	Ac	227	—	—
90	Th	232.05	11.2	2.94
91	Pa	231	15.4	4.02
92	U	238.07	18.7	4.73
93	Np	237	—	—
94	Pu	239	19.74	4.98

^{j} At 22.5°C.
^{k} Tetragonal (ordinary; β)
^{l} Metallic tantalum

TABLE 2

Properties of some common materials used in nuclear physics experiments[1]

Material	Chemical name or type	Composition	Density (g/cm³)	Volume resistivity (Ω-cm)	Manufacturer
Aquadag	Colloidal graphite dispersion in isopropyl alcohol	C, H, O (varies)			Acheson Colloids Co.
Celluloid	Cellulose acetate	$(C_9H_{13}O_7)_n$	1.23–1.34	10^{10}–10^{14}	
Cymel	Melamine and formaldehyde condensation product	C, H, O, N (varies)			American Cyanamid
Formvar	Polyvinyl { alconol acetate formal	C, H, O (varies)	1.214–1.229		Monsanto
Havar		Fe(17.9%), Co(42.5%) Cr(20.0%), Ni(13.0%) W(2.8%), Mo, Mn, C, Be (traces)	8.3		Hamilton Watch Co.
Hevimet		W(90%), Ni(7.5%), Cu(2.5%)	16.9–17.2		General Electric
Kapton[a]	Polyamide film	$(C_{22}H_{10}N_2O_4)_n$	1.08–1.14		DuPont
Kel-F	Chlorotrifluoroethylene polymer	$(CF_2CHCl)_n$	2.1047–2.1312	1.2×10^{18}	3M Corp.
Lucite (Plexiglas)	Acrylic (methyl methacrylate) resins	$(C_5H_8O_2)_n$	1.18–1.19	$>10^{14}$	DuPont; Rohm and Haas
Mica[b]	Muscovite (white mica)	$K_2O \cdot 3Al_2O_3 \cdot 6SiO_2 \cdot 2H_2O$	2.76–3.00		
Mylar[c]	Polyester film	$(C_{10}H_8O_4)_n$	1.380–1.395	10^{14}	DuPont
Nylon	Polyamides	$(C_{12}H_{22}N_2O_2)_n$	1.08–1.14	10^{12}–10^{15}	DuPont
Polyethylene (Polythene)		$(CH_2 : CH_2)_n$	0.910–0.965	$>10^{16}$	
Polystyrene (Styron)		$(C_6H_5CH : CH_2)_n$	0.98–1.10	$>10^{16}$	Dow Chemical
Teflon	Tetrafluoroethylene resin	$(CF_2)_n$	2.1–2.2	$>10^{18}$	DuPont
VYNS	Polyvinylchloride-acetate copolymer (solution)	CH_2CHCl (90%) $CH_2CHO_2CCH_3$ (10%)	1.36		Union Carbide
Zapon	Nitrocellulose in a blend of hydrocarbon solvents	C, H, O, N (varies)			Glidden

[a] Formerly known as H-Film. This material is ≈ 50 times more resistant to radiation damage than mylar.[c]

[b] Many types of mica are known; the one listed is merely typical.

[c] Mylar suffers radiation damage at doses greater than about 5×10^8 rads [A. M. Koehler et al., Nuclear Instr. and Meth. 33 (1965) 341].

[1] Some of the material in this table is taken from L. Yaffe, Preparation of Thin Films, Sources, and Targets, Ann. Rev. Nuclear Sci. 12 (1962) 153.

TABLE 3

Conversion factors for energy loss calculations[1]

$$\varepsilon(\text{in } 10^{-15} \text{ eV-cm}^2) \times A = dE/dx \,(\text{in keV-cm}^2/\text{mg})$$

Stopping material	Z	A	Stopping material	Z	A
H_2	1	598	Mn	25	11.0
He	2	150	Fe	26	10.8
Li	3	86.8	Co	27	10.2
Be	4	66.8	Ni	28	10.3
B	5	55.7	Cu	29	9.48
C	6	50.1	Zn	30	9.21
N_2	7	43.0	Ge	32	8.30
O_2	8	38.8	Kr	36	7.19
F	9	31.7	Mo	42	6.28
Ne	10	29.8	Pd	46	5.64
Na	11	26.2	Ag	47	5.58
Mg	12	24.8	Sn	50	5.07
Al	13	22.3	Sb	51	4.95
Si	14	21.5	Xe	54	4.59
P	15	19.4	Ta	73	3.33
S	16	18.8	W	74	3.27
Cl	17	17.0	Pt	78	3.09
A	18	15.1	Au	79	3.05
K	19	15.4	Hg	80	2.99
Ca	20	15.0	Pb	82	2.91
V	23	11.8	Bi	83	2.88
Cr	24	11.6	Air	(7.5)	20.79

[1] W. Whaling in *Handbuch der Physik*, ed. E. Flügge, Vol. 34 (Springer-Verlag, Berlin, 1958) p. 193.

TABLE 4

Physical constants[1]

Velocity of light	$c = 2.9979 \times 10^{10}$ cm/sec
	$c^2 = 8.988 \times 10^{20}$ erg/g
	$\quad = 931.478$ MeV/amu
Electronic charge	$e = 4.8030 \times 10^{-10}$ statcoulomb
	$\quad = 4.8030 \times 10^{-10}$ (erg-cm)$^{\frac{1}{2}}$
	$\quad = 1.6021 \times 10^{-19}$ C
	$\quad = 1.6021 \times 10^{-12}$ erg/V
	$\quad = 3.7946 \times 10^{-7}$ (MeV-cm)$^{\frac{1}{2}}$
	$e^2 = 1.440 \times 10^{-13}$ MeV-cm
	$1/e = 0.6242 \times 10^{13}\ (\mu\text{C})^{-1}$
Planck's constant	$h = 6.6256 \times 10^{-27}$ erg-sec
	$\quad = 4.1356 \times 10^{-21}$ MeV-sec
	$\hbar = 1.0545 \times 10^{-27}$ erg-sec
	$\quad = 6.58195 \times 10^{-22}$ MeV-sec
	$\hbar^2 = 4.3322 \times 10^{-43}$ (MeV-sec)^2
	$\hbar/m_0 c^2 = 1.2880 \times 10^{-21}$ sec
	$\hbar c = 3.1613 \times 10^{-17}$ erg-cm
	$\quad = 1.9732 \times 10^{-11}$ MeV-cm
	$(\hbar c)^2 = 389.36$ MeV^2-bn
	$e/\hbar c = 1.9231 \times 10^4$ (MeV-cm)$^{-\frac{1}{2}}$
	$(e/\hbar c)^2 = 3.6982 \times 10^8$ (MeV-cm)$^{-1}$
Boltzmann's constant	$k = 1.3805 \times 10^{-16}$ erg/deg
	$\quad = 0.8617 \times 10^{-4}$ eV/deg
	$1/k = 1.1605 \times 10^4$ deg/eV
Avogadro's number	$N = 6.0225 \times 10^{23}$ atoms/mole
Faraday	$F = Ne = 9.6487 \times 10^4$ C/mole
Loschmidt's number	$L = 2.687 \times 10^{19}$ cm^{-3} (0°C, 760 mm Hg)
	$\quad = 2.547 \times 10^{19}$ cm^{-3} (15°C, 760 mm Hg)
Atomic mass unit ($C^{12} \equiv 12$)	$M_\mu = N^{-1} = 1.6604 \times 10^{-24}$ g
	$\quad = 1\,822.83\ m_0$
	$M_\mu c^2 = 931.478 \pm 0.005$ MeV
Proton mass	$M_p c^2 = 938.256 \pm 0.005$ MeV
Neutron mass	$M_n c^2 = 939.550 \pm 0.005$ MeV
Electron mass	$m_0 = 9.1091 \times 10^{-28}$ g
	$\quad = 0.5486 \times 10^{-3}$ amu
	$m_0 c^2 = 511.006 \pm 0.002$ keV

[1] Basic values taken from E. R. Cohen and J. W. M. DuMond, Revs. Modern Phys. *37* (1965) 537.

TABLE 4

Physical constants (continued)

Specific electronic charge	$e/m_0 = 1.758\,8 \times 10^8$ C/g
Fine structure constant	$\alpha = e^2/\hbar c = 1/137.039$
	$\quad\quad = 7.297\,2 \times 10^{-3}$
Bohr orbit radius	$a_0 = \hbar^2/m_0 e^2 = 5.291\,7 \times 10^{-9}$ cm
	$\pi a_0^2 = 8.797 \times 10^7$ bn
Electron Compton wavelength/2π	$\lambda = \hbar/m_0 c = 3.861\,44 \times 10^{-11}$ cm
	$\pi \lambda_0^2 = 4.684\,3 \times 10^3$ bn
Classical electron radius	$r_0 = e^2/m_0 c^2 = 2.817\,8 \times 10^{-13}$ cm
	$\pi r_0^2 = 0.2494$ bn
Thomson cross section	$(8/3)\pi r_0^2 = 0.665\,16$ bn
Bohr magneton	$\mu_0 = e\hbar/2m_0 c = 0.578\,82 \times 10^{-8}$ eV/gauss
Nuclear magneton	$\mu_N = e\hbar/2M_p c = 0.315\,24 \times 10^{-11}$ eV/gauss
Energy conversion factor	1 eV $= 1.602\,1 \times 10^{-12}$ erg
Time	1 day $= 86\,400$ sec
	1 year $= 3.156 \times 10^7$ sec
Rate of disintegration	1 curie $= 3.70 \times 10^{10}$ dis./sec
	1 rutherford $= 10^7$ dis./sec

Natural units
    If $\hbar = 1$ and $c = 1$, then
        a) Mass, energy, and impulse are in units of cm^{-1}
        b) Angular momentum is dimensionless
        c) $e = 1/\sqrt{137}$
        d) 1 MeV $= 0.506 \times 10^{11} \text{ cm}^{-1}$
    If $\hbar = 1$, $c = 1$ and $m_0 = 1$, then
        a) 1 sec $= 7.764 \times 10^{20}$ natural units
        b) 1 cm $= 2.58 \times 10^{10}$ natural units
        c) 1 MeV $= 1.96$ natural units

TABLE 5

Kinematics of nuclear reactions and scattering

The nonrelativistic expressions for the energetics and solid-angle relations for nuclear reactions and scattering will be found in the accompanying table (overleaf). The material is adapted from the Los Alamos report edited by Jarmie and Seagrave.[1] More complete accounts of nuclear reaction kinematics are available.[2]

Some of the important nonrelativistic and relativistic equations are given below. (The notation is explained in the table overleaf.)

Nonrelativistic kinematics

$$\sqrt{E_3} = \frac{\sqrt{M_1 M_3 E_1}}{M_3 + M_4} \cos\psi \left(1 \pm \left\{1 + \frac{1 + M_4/M_3}{\cos^2\psi}\left[\frac{M_4}{M_1}\left(1 + \frac{Q}{E_1}\right) - 1\right]\right\}^{\frac{1}{2}}\right) \tag{5.1}$$

$$E_3 = \frac{M_1 M_3 E_1}{(M_3 + M_4)^2}\left\{2\cos^2\psi + \frac{M_4(M_3 + M_4)}{M_1 M_3}\left(\frac{Q}{E_1} - \frac{M_1}{M_4} + 1\right)\right.$$

$$\left. \pm 2\cos\psi\left[\cos^2\psi + \frac{M_4(M_3 + M_4)}{M_1 M_3}\left(\frac{Q}{E_1} - \frac{M_1}{M_4} + 1\right)\right]^{\frac{1}{2}}\right\} \tag{5.2}$$

$$Q = \frac{M_3 + M_4}{M_4}E_3 - \frac{M_4 - M_1}{M_4}E_1 - \frac{2\sqrt{M_1 M_3 E_1 E_3}}{M_4}\cos\psi . \tag{5.3}$$

If a particle x with mass M_1 produces a (x, n) reaction on a stationary target nucleus of atomic mass M_2, the nonrelativistic expression connecting the threshold energy E_{th} and the Q-value Q_0 is

$$|Q_0| = \frac{M_2}{M_1 + M_2}E_{\text{th}} \tag{5.4}$$

where $Q_0 < 0$.

Relativistic kinematics

The particles are labeled 1, 2, 3, 4 as in the table on the following page. But now we define

M = rest mass in MeV (i.e., $c = 1$)
T = kinetic energy
$E = T + M$ = total energy
P = relativistic momentum = $\sqrt{E^2 - M^2} = \sqrt{T^2 + 2MT}$
$E_T = T_1 + M_1 + M_2$
$A = 2M_2 T_1 + 2M_1 M_3 + 2M_2 M_3 + 2Q(M_1 + M_2 - M_3) - Q^2$
$B = E_T^2 - P_1^2 \cos^2\psi$
$\frac{\partial B}{\partial\psi} = 2P_1^2 \sin\psi \cos\psi$

$$T_3 = E_3 - M_3 = \frac{1}{2B}\left[E_T A \pm P_1 \cos\psi \sqrt{A^2 - 4M_3^2 B}\right] - M_3 \tag{5.5}$$

$$T_4 = E_4 - M_4 = E_T - E_3 - (M_1 + M_2 - M_3 - Q) \tag{5.6}$$

$$Q = M_1 + M_2 - M_3 - [M_1^2 + M_2^2 + M_3^2 + 2M_2 E_1 - 2E_3(E_1 + M_2) + 2P_1 P_3 \cos\psi]^{\frac{1}{2}} \tag{5.7}$$

$$\zeta = \sin^{-1}\left(\frac{P_3}{P_4}\sin\psi\right) \tag{5.8}$$

$$\frac{\partial T_3}{\partial\psi} = -\frac{E_3}{B}\frac{\partial B}{\partial\psi} \mp \frac{P_1}{2B}\frac{A^2 + 4M_3^2(E_T^2 - 2B)}{\sqrt{A^2 - 4M_3^2 B}}\sin\psi . \tag{5.9}$$

The relativistic expression for the threshold energy in terms of Q is

$$E_{\text{th}} = |Q|\left(\frac{M_1 + M_2}{M_2} + \frac{|Q|}{2M_2}\right) \tag{5.10}$$

so that in terms of Q_0, the nonrelativistic value [see eq. (5.4)], the true Q-value is

$$|Q| \cong |Q_0| - \frac{|Q_0|^2}{2(M_1 + M_2)} \tag{5.11}$$

[1] Charged Particle Cross Sections, N. Jarmie and J. D. Seagrave, eds., Los Alamos Scientific Laboratory Report LA-2014, unpublished (1957).
[2] See, for example, A. M. Baldin, V. I. Goldanskiǐ and I. L. Rozental', *Kinematics of Nuclear Reactions* (Oxford University Press, 1961).

140

TABLE 5

Kinematics of nuclear reactions and scattering (continued)

ψ, ζ in lab
θ, ϕ in C. M.
  Primed energies in C.M.

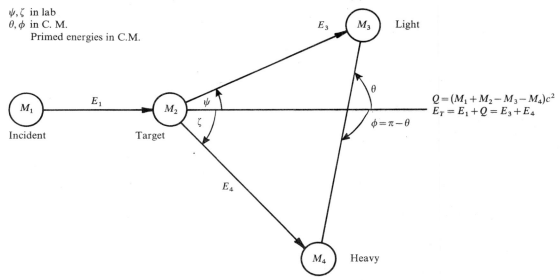

$Q = (M_1 + M_2 - M_3 - M_4)c^2$
$E_T = E_1 + Q = E_3 + E_4$

Define:

$$A = \frac{M_1 M_4 (E_1/E_T)}{(M_1 + M_2)(M_3 + M_4)}, \qquad C = \frac{M_2 M_3}{(M_1 + M_2)(M_3 + M_4)}\left(1 + \frac{M_1 Q}{M_2 E_T}\right) = \frac{E_4'}{E_T}$$

$$B = \frac{M_1 M_3 (E_1/E_T)}{(M_1 + M_2)(M_3 + M_4)}, \qquad D = \frac{M_2 M_4}{(M_1 + M_2)(M_3 + M_4)}\left(1 + \frac{M_1 Q}{M_2 E_T}\right) = \frac{E_3'}{E_T}$$

Note that $A + B + C + D = 1$ and $AC = BD$

Lab energy of light product:	$\dfrac{E_3}{E_T} = B + D + 2(AC)^{\frac{1}{2}} \cos \theta$ $\quad = B[\cos \psi \pm (D/B - \sin^2 \psi)^{\frac{1}{2}}]^2$	Use only plus sign unless $B > D$, in which case $\psi_{\max} = \sin^{-1}(D/B)^{\frac{1}{2}}$
Lab energy of heavy product:	$\dfrac{E_4}{E_T} = A + C + 2(AC)^{\frac{1}{2}} \cos \phi$ $\quad = A[\cos \zeta \pm (C/A - \sin^2 \zeta)^{\frac{1}{2}}]^2$	Use only plus sign unless $A > C$, in which case $\zeta_{\max} = \sin^{-1}(C/A)^{\frac{1}{2}}$
Lab angle of heavy product:	$\sin \zeta = \left(\dfrac{M_3 E_3}{M_4 E_4}\right)^{\frac{1}{2}} \sin \psi$ $\quad$ C.M. angle of light product: $\quad$ $\sin \theta = \left(\dfrac{E_3/E_T}{D}\right) \sin \psi$	
Intensity or solid-angle ratio for light product:	$\dfrac{\sigma(\theta)}{\sigma(\psi)} = \dfrac{I(\theta)}{I(\psi)} = \dfrac{\sin \psi \, d\psi}{\sin \theta \, d\theta} = \dfrac{\sin^2 \psi}{\sin^2 \theta} \cos(\theta - \psi) = \dfrac{(AC)^{\frac{1}{2}}(D/B - \sin^2 \psi)^{\frac{1}{2}}}{E_3/E_T}$	
Intensity or solid-angle ratio for heavy product:	$\dfrac{\sigma(\phi)}{\sigma(\zeta)} = \dfrac{I(\phi)}{I(\zeta)} = \dfrac{\sin \zeta \, d\zeta}{\sin \phi \, d\phi} = \dfrac{\sin^2 \zeta}{\sin^2 \phi} \cos(\phi - \zeta) = \dfrac{(AC)^{\frac{1}{2}}(C/A - \sin^2 \zeta)^{\frac{1}{2}}}{E_4/E_T}$	
Intensity or solid-angle ratio for associated particles in the lab system:	$\dfrac{\sigma(\zeta)}{\sigma(\psi)} = \dfrac{I(\zeta)}{I(\psi)} = \dfrac{\sin \psi \, d\psi}{\sin \zeta \, d\zeta} = \dfrac{\sin^2 \psi \cos(\theta - \psi)}{\sin^2 \zeta \cos(\phi - \zeta)}$	

TABLE 5

Kinematics of nuclear reactions and scattering (continued)

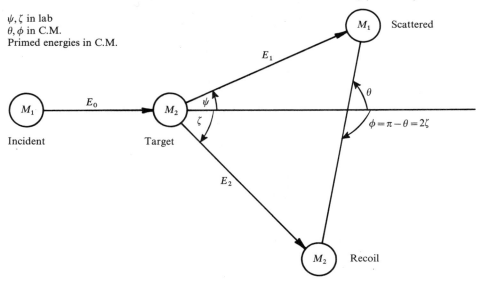

ψ, ζ in lab
θ, ϕ in C.M.
Primed energies in C.M.

$$E_1' = \frac{M_2^2}{(M_1 + M_2)^2} E_0$$

For elastic scattering, all energy and
angle ratios are independent of energy
and reduce as below:

$$E_2' = \frac{M_1 M_2}{(M_1 + M_2)^2} E_0$$

Lab energy of the scattered particle:	$\dfrac{E_1}{E_0} = 1 - \dfrac{2M_1 M_2}{(M_1 + M_2)^2}(1 - \cos\theta)$ $= \dfrac{M_1^2}{(M_1 + M_2)^2}\{\cos\psi \pm [(M_2/M_1)^2 - \sin^2\psi]^{\frac{1}{2}}\}^2$	Use only plus sign unless $M_1 > M_2$, in which case $\psi_{max} = \sin^{-1}(M_2/M_1)$
Lab energy of the recoil nucleus:	$\dfrac{E_2}{E_0} = 1 - E_1/E_0 = \dfrac{4M_1 M_2}{(M_1 + M_2)^2}\cos^2\zeta \qquad \zeta \leqq \tfrac{1}{2}\pi$	
Lab angle of recoil nucleus:	$\sin\zeta = \left(\dfrac{M_1 E_1}{M_2 E_2}\right)^{\frac{1}{2}}\sin\psi, \qquad \zeta = \tfrac{1}{2}(\pi - \phi), \qquad \tan\psi = \dfrac{\sin 2\zeta}{M_1/M_2 - \cos 2\zeta}$	
C.M. angle of scattered particle:	$\theta = \psi + \sin^{-1}\left(\dfrac{M_1}{M_2}\sin\psi\right) = \pi - 2\zeta \qquad \cos\theta = 1 - 2\cos^2\zeta$	
Intensity or solid-angle ratio for scattered particle:	$\dfrac{\sigma(\theta)}{\sigma(\psi)} = \dfrac{I(\theta)}{I(\psi)} = \dfrac{\sin\psi\,d\psi}{\sin\theta\,d\theta} = \dfrac{\sin^2\psi}{\sin^2\theta}\cos(\theta - \psi) = \dfrac{M_1 M_2 [(M_2/M_1)^2 - \sin^2\psi]^{\frac{1}{2}}}{(M_1 + M_2)^2(E_1/E_0)}$	
Intensity or solid-angle ratio for recoil nucleus:	$\dfrac{\sigma(\phi)}{\sigma(\zeta)} = \dfrac{I(\phi)}{I(\zeta)} = \dfrac{\sin\zeta\,d\zeta}{\sin\phi\,d\phi} = \dfrac{1}{4\cos\zeta}$	

TABLE 6

Alpha-particle calibration energies

Listed below are the values of α-particle momenta and energies recommended by Wapstra.[1] The energies have been calculated for Wapstra's $B\varrho$-values by using the expression (see Fig. 68)

$$E = a(B\varrho)^2 + b(B\varrho)^4 + c(B\varrho)^6$$

where a, b, and c are

$$a = 48\,225.33 \times 10^{-12} \text{ keV(G-cm)}^{-2}$$

$$b = -\,311.98 \times 10^{-24} \text{ keV(G-cm)}^{-4}$$

$$c = 4.04 \times 10^{-36} \text{ keV(G-cm)}^{-6}$$

Source	$B\varrho$ (G-cm)	Energy (keV)
Po^{210}	$331\,772 \pm 15$	$5\,304.5 \pm 0.5$
Bi^{211}	$370\,720 \pm 40$	$6\,621.9 \pm 1.4$
Po^{211}	$393\,190 \pm 50$	$7\,448.1 \pm 1.9$
$Bi^{212}(ThC\ \alpha_0)$*	$354\,326 \pm 20$	$6\,049.6 \pm 0.7$
$Bi^{212}(ThC\ \alpha_1)$*	$355\,475 \pm 20$	$6\,088.9 \pm 0.7$
$Po^{212}(ThC')$	$427\,060 \pm 20$	$8\,785.0 \pm 0.8$
Bi^{214}	$338\,170 \pm 70$	$5\,510.9 \pm 2.3$
Po^{214}	$399\,488 \pm 16$	$7\,688.4 \pm 0.6$
Po^{215}	$391\,490 \pm 40$	$7\,383.9 \pm 1.5$
Po^{216}	$375\,050 \pm 40$	$6\,777.3 \pm 1.5$
Po^{218}	$352\,870 \pm 70$	$6\,000.1 \pm 2.4$
Rn^{219}	$376\,160 \pm 40$	$6\,817.5 \pm 1.5$
Rn^{220}	$361\,260 \pm 60$	$6\,288.5 \pm 2.1$
Rn^{222}	$337\,410 \pm 70$	$5\,486.2 \pm 2.3$
Ra^{223}	$349\,010 \pm 50$	$5\,869.6 \pm 1.7$
Ra^{224}	$343\,450 \pm 40$	$5\,684.2 \pm 1.3$
Ra^{226}	$314\,990 \pm 80$	$4\,781.8 \pm 2.4$
Th^{227}	$354\,070 \pm 60$	$6\,040.9 \pm 2.0$
Th^{228}	$335\,570 \pm 60$	$5\,426.6 \pm 2.0$
Th^{230}	$311\,960 \pm 160$	$4\,690.3 \pm 4.8$

* Intensity ratio: $\alpha_0/\alpha_1 = 2.57$
[1] A. H. Wapstra, Nuclear Phys. 57 (1964) 48.

TABLE 7

Gamma-ray calibration energies

Listed below are the weighted mean values of the energies of gamma rays frequently used as calibration standards.[1] (A more comprehensive list may be found in Ref. 1.) Also, relative intensities are given for the case of Co^{56} since the gamma rays from this nucleus span such a wide energy range and are therefore of great value for both energy and efficiency calibrations. Gamma rays from both radioactive sources and nuclear reactions are given.

Gamma rays from radioactive sources

Source	Energy (keV)	Half-life	Co^{56} Energy (keV)	Co^{56} Relative intensity
m_0c^2	511.006 ± 0.002		733.79 ± 0.19	0.1 ± 0.05
Be^7	477.57 ± 0.05	53 d	787.92 ± 0.15	0.40 ± 0.11
Na^{22}	$1\,274.55 \pm 0.04$	2.60 y	846.76 ± 0.05	100
Na^{24}	$\{$ $1\,368.526 \pm 0.044$	15.0 h	977.47 ± 0.13	1.52 ± 0.16
	$2\,753.92 \pm 0.12$		$1\,037.97 \pm 0.07$	13.02 ± 0.35
Cr^{51}	320.080 ± 0.013	27.8 d	$1\,175.26 \pm 0.13$	1.86 ± 0.23
Mn^{54}	834.81 ± 0.03	314 d	$1\,238.34 \pm 0.09$	69.35 ± 1.47
Co^{60}	$\{$ $1\,173.23 \pm 0.04$	5.26 y	$1\,360.35 \pm 0.09$	4.38 ± 0.16
	$1\,332.49 \pm 0.04$		$1\,771.57 \pm 0.10$	15.30 ± 0.53
Zn^{65}	$1\,115.40 \pm 0.12$	246 d	$1\,964.88 \pm 0.45$	0.72 ± 0.08
Y^{88}	$\{$ 898.04 ± 0.04	106.6 d	$2\,015.49 \pm 0.20$	2.93 ± 0.16
	$1\,836.13 \pm 0.04$		$2\,035.03 \pm 0.12$	7.33 ± 0.30
Cs^{137}	661.635 ± 0.076	30 y	$2\,113.00 \pm 0.10$	0.37 ± 0.08
Au^{198}	411.795 ± 0.009	2.70 d	$2\,598.80 \pm 0.12$	16.77 ± 0.57
Bi^{207}	$\{$ 569.62 ± 0.06	30 y	$3\,009.99 \pm 0.24$	0.84 ± 0.16
	$1\,063.44 \pm 0.09$		$3\,202.25 \pm 0.19$	3.15 ± 0.16
	$1\,769.71 \pm 0.13$		$3\,253.82 \pm 0.15$	7.70 ± 0.34
Tl^{208} (ThC'')	$\{$ 510.723 ± 0.020	(1.91 y)	$3\,273.38 \pm 0.18$	1.55 ± 0.11
	583.139 ± 0.023		$3\,452.18 \pm 0.22$	0.88 ± 0.10
	$2\,614.47 \pm 0.10$		$3\,548.11 \pm 0.25$	0.18 ± 0.01
Am^{241}	$\{$ 26.348 ± 0.010	433 y		
	59.543 ± 0.015			

Gamma rays from nuclear reactions

Nucleus	γ-ray energy (keV)	Nucleus	γ-ray energy (keV)
F^{17}	495.33 ± 0.10	C^{13}	$4\,945.46 \pm 0.17^e$
F^{18}	658.75 ± 0.7^a	N^{14}	$5\,104.87 \pm 0.18$
O^{17}	870.81 ± 0.22	O^{15}	$5\,240.53 \pm 0.52$
B^{12}	953.10 ± 0.60	N^{15}	$5\,268.9 \pm 0.2$
B^{12}	$1\,673.52 \pm 0.60$	N^{15}	$5\,297.9 \pm 0.2^g$
N^{14}	$2\,312.68 \pm 0.10^b$	O^{16}	$6\,129.3 \pm 0.4$
Be^{10}	$2\,589.9 \pm 0.25^c$	Be^{10}	$6\,809.4 \pm 0.4^e$
N^{14}	$2\,792.68 \pm 0.15^d$	O^{16}	$7\,117.02 \pm 0.49$
Be^{10}	$3\,367.4 \pm 0.2^e$	Pb^{209}	$7\,367.5 \pm 1^e$
C^{12}	$4\,439.0 \pm 0.2^f$	N^{14}	$9\,173 \pm 1^h$
		N^{15}	$10\,829.2 \pm 0.4^e$

[a] From 1.70–1.04 MeV decay
[b] Doppler shifted unless formed in $O^{14}(\beta^+)N^{14}$
[c] From 5.96–3.37 MeV decay (thermal neutron capture)
[d] From 5.10–2.31 MeV decay
[e] From thermal neutron capture
[f] Doppler shifted unless formed in $B^{12}(\beta^-)C^{12}$
[g] Doppler shifted unless formed in $O^{15}(\beta^-)N^{15}$ or by thermal neutron capture
[h] Calculated from $C^{13}(p,\gamma)N^{14}$ resonance energy ($1\,747.6 \pm 0.9$ keV) and 1964 masses; value given for observation at $0°$ to beam direction.
[1] J. B. Marion, Nuclear Data (to be published).

TABLE 8

Accelerator energy calibration points

In order to know with precision the energy of the beam from an accelerator, unless an absolute instrument of some type is available, the beam analyzing system must be calibrated against some accurately known energy points. One method frequently used to calibrate such analyzers is to measure a number of γ-ray resonances and neutron thresholds to establish several points of the energy scale. Listed below are a number of energy points suitable for calibration purposes. Only the weighted mean values are given; more complete details can be found elsewhere.[1]

Proton resonances			Proton thresholds	
Reaction	E_R (keV)	Γ (keV)	Reaction	E_{th} (keV)
$F^{19}(p, \alpha\gamma)O^{16}$	340.46 ± 0.04	2.4 ± 0.2	$Li^7(p, n)Be^7$	$1\,880.60 \pm 0.07$
$F^{19}(p, \alpha\gamma)O^{16}$	872.11 ± 0.20	4.7 ± 0.2	$C^{13}(p, n)N^{13}$	$3\,235.7 \pm 0.7$
$Al^{27}(p, \gamma)Si^{28}$	991.90 ± 0.04	0.10 ± 0.02	$F^{19}(p, n)Ne^{19}$	$4\,234.3 \pm 0.8$
$C^{13}(p, \gamma)N^{14}$	$1\,747.6 \pm 0.9$	0.077 ± 0.012	$Al^{27}(p, n)Si^{27}$	$5\,796.9 \pm 3.8$
$O^{16}(p, p)O^{16}$	$12\,714 \pm 8^2$	< 3	$S^{34}(p, n)Cl^{34}$	$6\,451.1 \pm 4.5$
$C^{12}(p, p)C^{12}$	$14\,233 \pm 8$	< 1	$Ni^{60}(p, n)Cu^{60}$	$7\,023.6 \pm 3.9$
			$Fe^{54}(p, n)Co^{54}$	$9\,202.7 \pm 4.8$
			$Ni^{58}(p, n)Cu^{58}$	$9\,515.2 \pm 2.9$
			$C^{12}(p, n)N^{12}$	$19\,684 \pm 8$

Other useful calibration points are:

$O^{16}(d, n)F^{17}$	$E_{th} = 1\,829.2 \pm 0.6$ keV[3]
$Mg^{24}(\alpha, \gamma)Si^{28}$	$E_R = 3\,200 \pm 1$ keV[4]

Threshold energies for various helium-ion-induced reactions can be calculated from the 1964 adjustment of atomic masses:[5]

Reaction	E_{th} (MeV $\pm$ keV)
$Li^6(He^3, n)B^8$	2.9650 ± 1.5
$Li^6(\alpha, n)B^9$	6.6239 ± 2.6
$Li^7(\alpha, n)B^{10}$	4.3843 ± 1.9
$C^{12}(He^3, n)O^{14}$	1.4366 ± 0.5
$C^{12}(\alpha, n)O^{15}$	11.3463 ± 1.7
$N^{14}(\alpha, n)F^{17}$	6.0888 ± 0.8
$N^{15}(\alpha, n)F^{18}$	8.1324 ± 1.5
$O^{16}(He^3, n)Ne^{18}$	3.7987 ± 5.7
$O^{16}(\alpha, n)Ne^{19}$	15.1761 ± 2.0

[1] J. B. Marion, Revs. Modern Phys. *38* (1966) 660.
[2] J. R. Patterson, H. Winkler and C. S. Zaidins, Phys. Rev. *163* (1967) 1051.
[3] R. O. Bondelid, J. W. Butler and C. A. Kennedy, Phys. Rev. *120* (1960) 889.
[4] A. Rytz, H. Staub, H. Winkler and F. Zamboni, Nuclear Phys. *43* (1963) 229.
[5] J. H. E. Mattauch, W. Thiele and A. H. Wapstra, Nuclear Phys. *67* (1965) 73.

TABLE 9

Radiation and radiology units

1 R (roentgen)	– Quantity of X- or γ rays which will produce by ionization 1 electrostatic unit of electricity of either sign in 1 cm³ of dry air at NTP – 87.7 erg absorbed/g of air – $2 \times 10^9/E_\gamma$ (MeV) γ rays/cm² (accurate to $<15\%$ for $0.07 < E_\gamma < 2$ MeV) – 4.3×10^7 1-MeV β particles/cm²
1 R/hr	– 18 MeV/cm³(air)-sec
1 REP (roentgen equivalent, physical)	– 93 erg absorbed/g of water or tissue
1 Rad	– 100 erg absorbed/g of material
RBE (relative biological effectiveness)	– Effectiveness of any type of radiation in producing biological damage relative to the damage produced by – X- or γ rays of ≈ 200 keV – X- and γ rays, β's: RBE = 1 thermal neutrons: RBE = 2.5 1–10 MeV neutrons, protons, α particles: RBE = 10 heavy ions: RBE = 20
1 Rem (roentgen equivalent, man)	– 1 Rad × RBE – Quantity of radiation that produces the same biological damage in man as that caused by the absorption of 1 Rad of X- or γ rays
Maximum permissible dose of neutrons (for 40-hr week)	– Thermal: 670 n/cm²-sec 0.1 MeV: 80 0.5 MeV: 30 1 MeV: 18 10 MeV: 17 10–30 MeV: 10
Maximum permissible dose of all other types of radiation (for 40-hr week)	– 0.1 Rem

TABLE 10

Nuclear radii, sum-rule limits, wave numbers, and resonance cross sections

The quantities tabulated below are of use in the analysis of reactions induced by protons, deuterons, He^3 ions, and α particles on light- and medium-weight nuclei.

Definitions:

A_1 = mass number of the bombarding particle
A_2 = mass number of the target nucleus
E = laboratory energy of the bombarding particle (MeV)
M = reduced mass
μ $= A_1 A_2/(A_1 + A_2) =$ reduced mass number
η $= Z_1 Z_2 e^2/\hbar v = 0.1575\, Z_1 Z_2 \sqrt{A_1/E}$

The tabulated quantities are:

1) Interaction radius (fm): $R = R_0(A_1^{\frac{1}{3}} + A_2^{\frac{1}{3}})$, $R_0 = 1.40$

2) Sum-rule limit: $\theta^2 = \frac{3}{2}\dfrac{\hbar^2}{MR} = \dfrac{62.70}{\mu R}$ MeV-fm

3) $\qquad\qquad\qquad = \dfrac{62.70}{\mu R^2}$ MeV

4) Wave number: $k/\sqrt{E} = \mu/\sqrt{A_1} \times 0.218\,7 \times 10^{13}$ cm^{-1}-MeV$^{-\frac{1}{2}}$

5) $\pi E/k^2$ (MeV-barns) from the resonance cross section:

$$\sigma = \frac{2J+1}{(2S+1)(2I+1)}\frac{\pi}{k^2}\frac{\Gamma_1\Gamma_2}{(E-E_R)^2 + \frac{1}{4}\Gamma^2}$$

$$\sigma(E=E_R) = \omega\,\frac{\pi}{k^2}\,\frac{4\Gamma_1\Gamma_2}{\Gamma^2}$$

6) $\varrho/\sqrt{E}$ (MeV$^{-\frac{1}{2}}$) from $\varrho = kR$, $\varrho/\sqrt{E} = 0.218\,7\,\mu R/\sqrt{A_1}$

147

A_2	R (fm)	$\frac{3}{2}\dfrac{\hbar^2}{\mu R}$ (MeV-fm)	$\frac{3}{2}\dfrac{\hbar^2}{\mu R^2}$ (MeV)	$k/\sqrt{E} \times 10^{13}$ (cm^{-1}-MeV$^{-\frac{1}{2}}$)	$\dfrac{\pi}{k^2}E$ (barns-MeV)	$\varrho/\sqrt{E}$ (MeV$^{-\frac{1}{2}}$)
1	2.800	44.79	15.995	0.1093	2.627	0.306
2	3.164	29.73	9.395	0.1458	1.478	0.461
3	3.419	24.45	7.151	0.1640	1.168	0.561
4	3.622	21.64	5.973	0.1750	1.026	0.634
5	3.794	19.83	5.227	0.1822	0.946	0.691
6	3.944	18.55	4.703	0.1875	0.894	0.739
7	4.078	17.57	4.309	0.1914	0.858	0.780
8	4.200	16.79	3.999	0.1944	0.831	0.816
9	4.312	16.16	3.747	0.1968	0.811	0.849
10	4.416	15.62	3.536	0.1988	0.795	0.878
11	4.514	15.15	3.357	0.2005	0.782	0.905
12	4.605	14.75	3.203	0.2019	0.771	0.930
13	4.692	14.39	3.067	0.2031	0.762	0.953
14	4.774	14.07	2.947	0.2041	0.754	0.975
15	4.853	13.78	2.840	0.2050	0.747	0.995
16	4.928	13.52	2.743	0.2058	0.741	1.014
17	5.000	13.28	2.656	0.2065	0.736	1.033
18	5.069	13.06	2.576	0.2072	0.732	1.050
19	5.136	12.85	2.502	0.2078	0.728	1.067
20	5.200	12.66	2.435	0.2083	0.724	1.083
21	5.262	12.48	2.372	0.2088	0.721	1.099
22	5.323	12.31	2.314	0.2092	0.718	1.113
23	5.381	12.16	2.259	0.2096	0.715	1.128
24	5.438	12.01	2.208	0.2100	0.713	1.142
25	5.494	11.87	2.161	0.2103	0.710	1.155
26	5.547	11.74	2.116	0.2106	0.708	1.168
27	5.600	11.61	2.073	0.2109	0.706	1.181
28	5.651	11.49	2.033	0.2112	0.705	1.193
29	5.701	11.38	1.995	0.2114	0.703	1.205
30	5.750	11.27	1.960	0.2116	0.701	1.217
31	5.798	11.16	1.925	0.2119	0.700	1.228
32	5.845	11.06	1.893	0.2121	0.699	1.240
33	5.891	10.97	1.862	0.2123	0.697	1.250
34	5.935	10.87	1.832	0.2125	0.696	1.261
35	5.979	10.79	1.804	0.2126	0.695	1.271
36	6.023	10.70	1.777	0.2128	0.694	1.282
37	6.065	10.62	1.751	0.2129	0.693	1.292
38	6.107	10.54	1.726	0.2131	0.692	1.301
39	6.148	10.46	1.702	0.2132	0.691	1.311
40	6.188	10.39	1.678	0.2134	0.690	1.320
41	6.228	10.31	1.656	0.2135	0.689	1.330
42	6.266	10.24	1.635	0.2136	0.688	1.339
43	6.305	10.18	1.614	0.2137	0.688	1.348
44	6.342	10.11	1.594	0.2138	0.687	1.356
45	6.380	10.05	1.575	0.2139	0.686	1.365
46	6.416	9.98	1.556	0.2140	0.686	1.373
47	6.452	9.92	1.538	0.2141	0.685	1.382
48	6.488	9.87	1.521	0.2142	0.684	1.390
49	6.523	9.81	1.504	0.2143	0.684	1.398
50	6.558	9.75	1.487	0.2144	0.683	1.406
51	6.592	9.70	1.471	0.2145	0.683	1.414
52	6.626	9.65	1.456	0.2146	0.682	1.422
53	6.659	9.59	1.441	0.2146	0.682	1.429
54	6.692	9.54	1.426	0.2147	0.681	1.437
55	6.724	9.49	1.412	0.2148	0.681	1.444
56	6.756	9.45	1.398	0.2149	0.680	1.452
57	6.788	9.40	1.385	0.2149	0.680	1.459
58	6.819	9.35	1.372	0.2150	0.680	1.466
59	6.850	9.31	1.359	0.2151	0.679	1.473
60	6.881	9.26	1.346	0.2151	0.679	1.480

Deuterons: $A_1 = 2$; $Z_1 = 1$; $R_0 = 1.40$ fm; $\eta\sqrt{E}/Z_2 = 0.2227$

A_2	R (fm)	$\frac{3}{2}\dfrac{\hbar^2}{\mu R}$ (MeV-fm)	$\frac{3}{2}\dfrac{\hbar^2}{\mu R^2}$ (MeV)	$k/\sqrt{E} \times 10^{13}$ (cm^{-1}-MeV$^{-\frac{1}{2}}$)	$\dfrac{\pi}{k^2}E$ (barns-MeV)	$\varrho/\sqrt{E}$ (MeV$^{-\frac{1}{2}}$)
1	3.164	29.73	9.395	0.1031	2.956	0.326
2	3.528	17.77	5.038	0.1546	1.314	0.546
3	3.783	13.81	3.651	0.1856	0.912	0.702
4	3.986	11.80	2.959	0.2062	0.739	0.822
5	4.158	10.56	2.539	0.2209	0.644	0.919
6	4.308	9.70	2.252	0.2320	0.584	0.999
7	4.442	9.07	2.043	0.2406	0.543	1.069
8	4.564	8.59	1.881	0.2474	0.513	1.129
9	4.676	8.19	1.752	0.2531	0.491	1.183
10	4.780	7.87	1.646	0.2577	0.473	1.232
11	4.877	7.60	1.557	0.2617	0.459	1.276
12	4.969	7.36	1.481	0.2651	0.447	1.317
13	5.056	7.15	1.415	0.2681	0.437	1.355
14	5.138	6.97	1.357	0.2706	0.429	1.391
15	5.217	6.81	1.306	0.2729	0.422	1.424
16	5.292	6.66	1.260	0.2749	0.416	1.455
17	5.364	6.53	1.218	0.2767	0.410	1.484
18	5.433	6.41	1.180	0.2784	0.405	1.512
19	5.500	6.30	1.146	0.2798	0.401	1.539
20	5.564	6.20	1.114	0.2812	0.397	1.564
21	5.626	6.10	1.085	0.2824	0.394	1.589
22	5.687	6.01	1.058	0.2835	0.391	1.612
23	5.745	5.93	1.032	0.2845	0.388	1.635
24	5.802	5.85	1.009	0.2855	0.385	1.657
25	5.858	5.78	0.987	0.2864	0.383	1.677
26	5.911	5.71	0.966	0.2872	0.381	1.698
27	5.964	5.65	0.947	0.2880	0.379	1.717
28	6.015	5.58	0.928	0.2887	0.377	1.736
29	6.065	5.53	0.911	0.2893	0.375	1.755
30	6.114	5.47	0.895	0.2900	0.374	1.773
31	6.162	5.42	0.879	0.2905	0.372	1.790
32	6.209	5.37	0.864	0.2911	0.371	1.807
33	6.254	5.32	0.850	0.2916	0.369	1.824
34	6.299	5.27	0.837	0.2921	0.368	1.840
35	6.343	5.22	0.824	0.2926	0.367	1.856
36	6.387	5.18	0.811	0.2930	0.366	1.871
37	6.429	5.14	0.799	0.2934	0.365	1.886
38	6.471	5.10	0.788	0.2938	0.364	1.901
39	6.512	5.06	0.777	0.2942	0.363	1.916
40	6.552	5.02	0.767	0.2946	0.362	1.930
41	6.591	4.99	0.757	0.2949	0.361	1.944
42	6.630	4.95	0.747	0.2952	0.360	1.957
43	6.669	4.92	0.738	0.2955	0.360	1.971
44	6.706	4.89	0.729	0.2958	0.359	1.984
45	6.744	4.86	0.720	0.2961	0.358	1.997
46	6.780	4.82	0.712	0.2964	0.358	2.010
47	6.816	4.80	0.703	0.2967	0.357	2.022
48	6.852	4.77	0.696	1.2969	0.356	2.034
49	6.887	4.74	0.688	0.2972	0.356	2.047
50	6.922	4.71	0.681	0.2974	0.355	2.058
51	6.956	4.68	0.673	0.2976	0.355	2.070
52	6.989	4.66	0.666	0.2978	0.354	2.082
53	7.023	4.63	0.660	0.2980	0.354	2.093
54	7.056	4.61	0.653	0.2982	0.353	2.104
55	7.088	4.58	0.647	0.2984	0.353	2.115
56	7.120	4.56	0.640	0.2986	0.352	2.126
57	7.152	4.54	0.634	0.2988	0.352	2.137
58	7.183	4.51	0.629	0.2990	0.351	2.148
59	7.214	4.49	0.623	0.2991	0.351	2.158
60	7.245	4.47	0.617	0.2993	0.351	2.168

$$\text{He}^3 : A_1 = 3 ; Z_1 = 2 ; R_0 = 1.40 \text{ fm} ; \eta\sqrt{E}/Z_2 = 0.5456$$

A_2	R (fm)	$\frac{3}{2}\frac{\hbar^2}{\mu R}$ (MeV-fm)	$\frac{3}{2}\frac{\hbar^2}{\mu R^2}$ (MeV)	$k/\sqrt{E} \times 10^{13}$ (cm^{-1}-MeV$^{-\frac{1}{2}}$)	$\frac{\pi}{k^2}E$ (barns-MeV)	$\varrho/\sqrt{E}$ (MeV$^{-\frac{1}{2}}$)
1	3.419	24.45	7.151	0.0947	3.503	0.324
2	3.783	13.81	3.651	0.1515	1.368	0.573
3	4.038	10.35	2.563	0.1894	0.876	0.765
4	4.242	8.62	2.033	0.2165	0.671	0.918
5	4.413	7.58	1.717	0.2367	0.560	1.045
6	4.563	6.87	1.506	0.2525	0.493	1.152
7	4.697	6.36	1.353	0.2652	0.447	1.246
8	4.819	5.96	1.237	0.2755	0.414	1.328
9	4.931	5.65	1.146	0.2841	0.389	1.401
10	5.035	5.40	1.072	0.2914	0.370	1.467
11	5.133	5.18	1.010	0.2976	0.355	1.528
12	5.224	5.00	0.957	0.3030	0.342	1.583
13	5.311	4.84	0.912	0.3078	0.332	1.635
14	5.393	4.71	0.872	0.3120	0.323	1.682
15	5.472	4.58	0.838	0.3157	0.315	1.727
16	5.547	4.47	0.807	0.3190	0.309	1.769
17	5.619	4.38	0.779	0.3220	0.303	1.809
18	5.688	4.29	0.754	0.3247	0.298	1.847
19	5.755	4.21	0.731	0.3271	0.294	1.883
20	5.819	4.13	0.710	0.3294	0.290	1.917
21	5.882	4.06	0.690	0.3314	0.286	1.949
22	5.942	4.00	0.673	0.3333	0.283	1.981
23	6.001	3.94	0.656	0.3351	0.280	2.011
24	6.057	3.88	0.641	0.3367	0.277	2.040
25	6.113	3.83	0.626	0.3382	0.275	2.067
26	6.167	3.78	0.613	0.3396	0.272	2.094
27	6.219	3.73	0.600	0.3409	0.270	2.120
28	6.270	3.69	0.589	0.3421	0.268	2.145
29	6.320	3.65	0.577	0.3433	0.267	2.170
30	6.369	3.61	0.567	0.3444	0.265	2.193
31	6.417	3.57	0.557	0.3454	0.263	2.216
32	6.464	3.54	0.547	0.3463	0.262	2.239
33	6.510	3.50	0.538	0.3472	0.261	2.260
34	6.555	3.47	0.529	0.3481	0.259	2.282
35	6.599	3.44	0.521	0.3489	0.258	2.302
36	6.642	3.41	0.513	0.3497	0.257	2.322
37	6.684	3.38	0.506	0.3504	0.256	2.342
38	6.726	3.35	0.498	0.3511	0.255	2.361
39	6.767	3.33	0.492	0.3517	0.254	2.380
40	6.807	3.30	0.485	0.3524	0.253	2.399
41	6.847	3.28	0.478	0.3530	0.252	2.417
42	6.886	3.25	0.472	0.3535	0.251	2.434
43	6.924	3.23	0.466	0.3541	0.251	2.452
44	6.962	3.21	0.461	0.3546	0.250	2.469
45	6.999	3.19	0.455	0.3551	0.249	2.485
46	7.035	3.16	0.450	0.3556	0.248	2.502
47	7.072	3.14	0.445	0.3561	0.248	2.518
48	7.107	3.12	0.440	0.3565	0.247	2.534
49	7.142	3.11	0.435	0.3569	0.247	2.549
50	7.177	3.09	0.430	0.3574	0.246	2.565
51	7.211	3.07	0.426	0.3578	0.245	2.580
52	7.245	3.05	0.421	0.3581	0.245	2.595
53	7.278	3.03	0.417	0.3585	0.244	2.609
54	7.311	3.02	0.413	0.3589	0.244	2.624
55	7.343	3.00	0.409	0.3592	0.243	2.638
56	7.375	2.99	0.405	0.3595	0.243	2.652
57	7.407	2.97	0.401	0.3599	0.243	2.665
58	7.438	2.96	0.397	0.3602	0.242	2.679
59	7.469	2.94	0.394	0.3605	0.242	2.692
60	7.500	2.93	0.390	0.3608	0.241	2.706

$$\text{He}^4: A_1=4;\ Z_1=2;\ R_0=1.40\text{ fm};\ \eta=\sqrt{E}/Z_2=0.6300$$

A_2	R (fm)	$\frac{3}{2}\frac{\hbar^2}{\mu R}$ (MeV-fm)	$\frac{3}{2}\frac{\hbar^2}{\mu R^2}$ (MeV)	$k/\sqrt{E}\times10^{13}$ (cm^{-1}-MeV$^{-\frac14}$)	$\frac{\pi}{k^2}E$ (barns-MeV)	$\varrho/\sqrt{E}$ (MeV$^{-\frac14}$)
1	3.622	21.64	5.973	0.0875	4.105	0.317
2	3.986	11.80	2.959	0.1458	1.478	0.581
3	4.242	8.62	2.033	0.1875	0.894	0.795
4	4.445	7.05	1.587	0.2187	0.657	0.972
5	4.616	6.11	1.324	0.2430	0.532	1.122
6	4.766	5.48	1.150	0.2624	0.456	1.251
7	4.900	5.03	1.026	0.2783	0.405	1.364
8	5.022	4.68	0.932	0.2916	0.369	1.465
9	5.134	4.41	0.859	0.3028	0.343	1.555
10	5.239	4.19	0.800	0.3124	0.322	1.637
11	5.336	4.01	0.751	0.3208	0.305	1.712
12	5.428	3.85	0.709	0.3280	0.292	1.781
13	5.514	3.72	0.674	0.3345	0.281	1.844
14	5.597	3.60	0.643	0.3402	0.271	1.904
15	5.675	3.50	0.616	0.3453	0.263	1.960
16	5.750	3.41	0.593	0.3499	0.257	2.012
17	5.822	3.33	0.571	0.3541	0.251	2.062
18	5.891	3.25	0.552	0.3579	0.245	2.108
19	5.958	3.18	0.535	0.3613	0.241	2.153
20	6.023	3.12	0.519	0.3645	0.236	2.195
21	6.085	3.07	0.504	0.3674	0.233	2.236
22	6.145	3.01	0.491	0.3701	0.229	2.274
23	6.204	2.97	0.478	0.3726	0.226	2.312
24	6.261	2.92	0.467	0.3749	0.224	2.347
25	6.316	2.88	0.456	0.3771	0.221	2.382
26	6.370	2.84	0.446	0.3791	0.219	2.415
27	6.422	2.80	0.436	0.3810	0.216	2.447
28	6.474	2.77	0.427	0.3827	0.214	2.478
29	6.524	2.73	0.419	0.3844	0.213	2.508
30	6.572	2.70	0.411	0.3859	0.211	2.537
31	6.620	2.67	0.404	0.3874	0.209	2.565
32	6.667	2.64	0.397	0.3888	0.208	2.592
33	6.713	2.62	0.390	0.3901	0.206	2.619
34	6.758	2.59	0.384	0.3914	0.205	2.645
35	6.802	2.57	0.378	0.3925	0.204	2.670
36	6.845	2.54	0.372	0.3937	0.203	2.695
37	6.887	2.52	0.366	0.3947	0.202	2.719
38	6.929	2.50	0.361	0.3957	0.201	2.742
39	6.970	2.48	0.356	0.3967	0.200	2.765
40	7.010	2.46	0.351	0.3976	0.199	2.788
41	7.050	2.44	0.346	0.3985	0.198	2.810
42	7.089	2.42	0.342	0.3994	0.197	2.831
43	7.127	2.40	0.337	0.4002	0.196	2.852
44	7.165	2.39	0.333	0.4009	0.195	2.873
45	7.202	2.37	0.329	0.4017	0.195	2.893
46	7.239	2.35	0.325	0.4024	0.194	2.913
47	7.275	2.34	0.321	0.4031	0.193	2.932
48	7.310	2.32	0.318	0.4038	0.193	2.952
49	7.345	2.31	0.314	0.4044	0.192	2.970
50	7.380	2.29	0.311	0.4050	0.192	2.989
51	7.414	2.28	0.308	0.4056	0.191	3.007
52	7.448	2.27	0.304	0.4062	0.190	3.025
53	7.481	2.25	0.301	0.4067	0.190	3.043
54	7.514	2.24	0.298	0.4072	0.189	3.060
55	7.546	2.23	0.295	0.4077	0.189	3.077
56	7.579	2.22	0.292	0.4082	0.189	3.094
57	7.610	2.20	0.290	0.4087	0.188	3.110
58	7.642	2.19	0.287	0.4092	0.188	3.127
59	7.673	2.18	0.284	0.4096	0.187	3.143
60	7.703	2.17	0.282	0.4101	0.187	3.159

TABLE 11

The accompanying table gives the velocities and times-of-flight (for 1 meter) for neutrons in the energy range $0.005 \leq E_n \leq 200$ MeV. These values were calculated from the relativistic expression,

$$v_n = c \left[1 - \frac{1}{(1 + E_n/939.550)^2} \right]^{\frac{1}{2}} \tag{11.1}$$

Approximate values can be obtained for other particles by scaling by the square root of the mass.

E_n (MeV)	Velocity (10^9 cm/sec)	T (ns/m)	E_n (MeV)	Velocity (10^9 cm/sec)	T (ns/m)	E_n (MeV)	Velocity (10^9 cm/sec)	T (ns/m)
0.005	0.098	1022.642	1.750	1.827	54.729	4.350	2.875	34.785
0.010	0.138	723.117	1.800	1.853	53.966	4.400	2.891	34.588
0.015	0.169	590.423	1.850	1.879	53.233	4.450	2.907	34.394
0.020	0.196	511.321	1.900	1.904	52.530	4.500	2.924	34.204
0.025	0.219	457.339	1.950	1.928	51.855	4.550	2.940	34.017
0.030	0.240	417.492	2.000	1.953	51.204	4.600	2.956	33.833
0.035	0.259	386.522	2.050	1.977	50.578	4.650	2.972	33.652
0.040	0.277	361.495	2.100	2.001	49.974	4.700	2.987	33.474
0.045	0.293	340.841	2.150	2.025	49.392	4.750	3.003	33.298
0.050	0.309	323.354	2.200	2.048	48.829	4.800	3.019	33.126
0.055	0.324	308.309	2.250	2.071	48.286	4.850	3.034	32.956
0.060	0.339	295.194	2.300	2.094	47.760	4.900	3.050	32.789
0.065	0.353	283.615	2.350	2.116	47.251	4.950	3.065	32.624
0.070	0.366	273.299	2.400	2.139	46.758	5.000	3.081	32.462
0.075	0.379	264.039	2.450	2.161	46.280	5.050	3.096	32.302
0.080	0.391	255.633	2.500	2.183	45.817	5.100	3.111	32.144
0.085	0.403	248.007	2.550	2.204	45.367	5.150	3.126	31.989
0.090	0.415	241.020	2.600	2.226	44.931	5.200	3.141	31.836
0.095	0.426	234.597	2.650	2.247	44.506	5.250	3.156	31.686
0.100	0.437	228.662	2.700	2.268	44.094	5.300	3.171	31.537
0.150	0.536	186.706	2.750	2.289	43.693	5.350	3.186	31.391
0.200	0.618	161.691	2.800	2.309	43.303	5.400	3.200	31.246
0.250	0.691	144.629	2.850	2.330	42.923	5.450	3.215	31.104
0.300	0.757	132.033	2.900	2.350	42.553	5.500	3.230	30.963
0.350	0.818	122.241	2.950	2.370	42.193	5.550	3.244	30.825
0.400	0.874	114.351	3.000	2.390	41.841	5.600	3.259	30.688
0.450	0.928	107.817	3.050	2.410	41.499	5.650	3.273	30.553
0.500	0.978	102.286	3.100	2.429	41.164	5.700	3.287	30.420
0.550	1.025	97.531	3.150	2.449	40.838	5.750	3.302	30.289
0.600	1.071	93.382	3.200	2.468	40.519	5.800	3.316	30.159
0.650	1.115	89.722	3.250	2.487	40.208	5.850	3.330	30.031
0.700	1.157	86.462	3.300	2.506	39.904	5.900	3.344	29.905
0.750	1.197	83.534	3.350	2.525	39.606	5.950	3.358	29.780
0.800	1.236	80.884	3.400	2.544	39.316	6.000	3.372	29.657
0.850	1.274	78.472	3.450	2.562	39.031	6.050	3.386	29.535
0.900	1.311	76.264	3.500	2.580	38.753	6.100	3.400	29.415
0.950	1.347	74.233	3.550	2.599	38.481	6.150	3.413	29.296
1.000	1.382	72.356	3.600	2.617	38.214	6.200	3.427	29.179
1.050	1.416	70.616	3.650	2.635	37.953	6.250	3.441	29.063
1.100	1.449	68.995	3.700	2.653	37.697	6.300	3.454	28.949
1.150	1.482	67.481	3.750	2.670	37.446	6.350	3.468	28.836
1.200	1.514	66.063	3.800	2.688	37.201	6.400	3.481	28.724
1.250	1.545	64.730	3.850	2.706	36.960	6.450	3.495	28.614
1.300	1.575	63.476	3.900	2.723	36.724	6.500	3.508	28.505
1.350	1.605	62.292	3.950	2.740	36.492	6.550	3.522	28.397
1.400	1.635	61.171	4.000	2.758	36.264	6.600	3.535	28.290
1.450	1.664	60.110	4.050	2.775	36.041	6.650	3.548	28.185
1.500	1.692	59.102	4.100	2.792	35.822	6.700	3.561	28.080
1.550	1.720	58.143	4.150	2.808	35.607	6.750	3.574	27.977
1.600	1.747	57.230	4.200	2.825	35.396	6.800	3.587	27.875
1.650	1.774	56.358	4.250	2.842	35.189	6.850	3.600	27.775
1.700	1.801	55.526	4.300	2.858	34.985	6.900	3.613	27.675

TABLE 11

Velocities and flight times for neutrons (continued)

E_n (MeV)	Velocity (10^9 cm/sec)	T (ns/m)	E_n (MeV)	Velocity (10^9 cm/sec)	T (ns/m)	E_n (MeV)	Velocity (10^9 cm/sec)	T (ns/m)
6.950	3.626	27.576	9.400	4.209	23.758	17.400	5.691	17.572
7.000	3.639	27.479	9.450	4.220	23.696	17.600	5.723	17.475
7.050	3.652	27.382	9.500	4.231	23.634	17.800	5.754	17.379
7.100	3.665	27.287	9.550	4.242	23.573	18.000	5.785	17.285
7.150	3.678	27.192	9.600	4.253	23.513	18.200	5.817	17.192
7.200	3.690	27.099	9.650	4.264	23.453	18.400	5.848	17.101
7.250	3.703	27.006	9.700	4.275	23.393	18.600	5.878	17.012
7.300	3.715	26.914	9.750	4.286	23.334	18.800	5.909	16.924
7.350	3.728	26.824	9.800	4.296	23.275	19.000	5.939	16.837
7.400	3.741	26.734	9.850	3.307	23.217	19.200	5.970	16.752
7.450	3.753	26.645	9.900	4.318	23.159	19.400	6.000	16.668
7.500	3.765	26.557	9.950	4.329	23.102	19.600	6.030	16.585
7.550	3.778	26.470	10.000	4.339	23.045	19.800	6.059	16.504
7.600	3.790	26.384	10.200	4.382	22.821	20.000	6.089	16.423
7.650	3.802	26.299	10.400	4.424	22.604	22.000	6.376	15.683
7.700	3.815	26.214	10.600	4.466	22.394	24.000	6.649	15.039
7.750	3.827	26.131	10.800	4.507	22.189	26.000	6.910	14.471
7.800	3.839	26.048	11.000	4.548	21.990	28.000	7.160	13.967
7.850	3.851	25.966	11.200	4.588	21.796	30.000	7.400	13.514
7.900	3.863	25.885	11.400	4.628	21.607	32.000	7.631	13.105
7.950	3.875	25.804	11.600	4.668	21.424	34.000	7.854	12.733
8.000	3.887	25.724	11.800	4.707	21.245	36.000	8.069	12.393
8.050	3.899	25.645	12.000	4.746	21.070	38.000	8.277	12.081
8.100	3.911	25.567	12.200	4.785	20.900	40.000	8.479	11.793
8.150	3.923	25.489	12.400	4.823	20.734	42.000	8.676	11.526
8.200	3.935	25.413	12.600	4.861	20.572	44.000	8.866	11.279
8.250	3.947	25.336	12.800	4.899	20.414	46.000	9.052	11.047
8.300	3.959	25.261	13.000	4.936	20.259	48.000	9.233	10.831
8.350	3.970	25.186	13.200	4.973	20.109	50.000	9.409	10.628
8.400	3.982	25.112	13.400	5.010	19.961	55.000	9.831	10.172
8.450	3.994	25.039	13.600	5.046	19.817	60.000	10.230	9.775
8.500	4.005	24.966	13.800	5.082	19.676	65.000	10.609	9.426
8.550	4.017	24.894	14.000	5.118	19.538	70.000	10.969	9.117
8.600	4.029	24.822	14.200	5.154	19.403	75.000	11.312	8.840
8.650	4.040	24.752	14.400	5.189	19.271	80.000	11.641	8.590
8.700	4.052	24.681	14.600	5.224	19.141	85.000	11.956	8.364
8.750	4.063	24.612	14.800	5.259	19.014	90.000	12.258	8.158
8.800	4.075	24.543	15.000	5.294	18.890	95.000	12.549	7.969
8.850	4.086	24.474	15.200	5.328	18.768	100.000	12.829	7.795
8.900	4.097	24.406	15.400	5.362	18.649	110.000	13.361	7.484
8.950	4.109	24.339	15.600	5.396	18.532	120.000	13.858	7.216
9.000	4.120	24.272	15.800	5.430	18.417	130.000	14.325	6.981
9.050	4.131	24.206	16.000	5.463	18.305	140.000	14.764	6.773
9.100	4.142	24.140	16.200	5.496	18.194	150.000	15.180	6.588
9.150	4.154	24.075	16.400	5.529	18.086	160.000	15.573	6.421
9.200	4.165	24.011	16.600	5.562	17.979	170.000	15.947	6.271
9.250	4.176	23.947	16.800	5.595	17.875	180.000	16.302	6.134
9.300	4.187	23.883	17.000	5.627	17.772	190.000	16.641	6.009
9.350	4.198	23.820	17.200	5.659	17.671	200.000	16.964	5.895

TABLE 12

The center-of-mass and laboratory cross sections for the Rutherford scattering of particles of mass M_1, charge $Z_1 e$, and incident laboratory energy E (MeV) by a target consisting of particles of mass M_2 and charge $Z_2 e$ are:

$$\left(\frac{d\sigma}{d\Omega}\right)_{\text{C.M.}} = 1.296 \left(\frac{Z_1 Z_2}{E}\right)^2 \left(\frac{M_1 + M_2}{M_2}\right)^2 \frac{1}{\sin^4(\tfrac{1}{2}\theta)} \text{ mb/sr} \tag{12.1}$$

$$\left(\frac{d\sigma}{d\Omega}\right)_{\text{lab}} = 1.296 \left(\frac{Z_1 Z_2}{E}\right)^2 \left[\csc^4(\tfrac{1}{2}\psi) - 2\left(\frac{M_1}{M_2}\right)^2 + \ldots\right] \text{ mb/sr} \tag{12.2}$$

where the next term in the last expression is of order $(M_1/M_2)^4$.

The accompanying table lists the values of $1/\sin^4(\tfrac{1}{2}\alpha)$ for $1° \leqq \alpha \leqq 180°$. The numbers in parentheses indicate the power of 10 by which the preceding number is to be multiplied.

A similar tabulation, but in intervals of 0.1°, has been given by Kim et al.[1]

α	$\dfrac{1}{\sin^4(\tfrac{1}{2}\alpha)}$	α	$\dfrac{1}{\sin^4(\tfrac{1}{2}\alpha)}$	α	$\dfrac{1}{\sin^4(\tfrac{1}{2}\alpha)}$
1.	1.724(8)	45.	4.663(1)	89.	4.143(0)
2.	1.078(7)	46.	4.290(1)	90.	4.000(0)
3.	2.130(6)	47.	3.955(1)	91.	3.864(0)
4.	6.741(5)	48.	3.654(0)	92.	3.735(0)
5.	2.762(5)	49.	3.381(1)	93.	3.612(0)
6.	1.333(5)	50.	3.135(1)	94.	3.495(0)
7.	7.199(4)	51.	2.911(1)	95.	3.384(0)
8.	4.223(4)	52.	2.708(1)	96.	3.279(0)
9.	2.639(4)	53.	2.523(1)	97.	3.178(0)
10.	1.733(4)	54.	2.354(1)	98.	3.082(0)
11.	1.185(4)	55.	2.200(1)	99.	2.991(0)
12.	8.376(3)	56.	2.059(1)	100.	2.904(0)
13.	6.089(3)	57.	1.929(1)	101.	2.821(0)
14.	4.533(3)	58.	1.810(1)	102.	2.742(0)
15.	3.445(3)	59.	1.701(1)	103.	2.666(0)
16.	2.666(3)	60.	1.600(1)	104.	2.593(0)
17.	2.095(3)	61.	1.507(1)	105.	2.524(0)
18.	1.670(3)	62.	1.421(1)	106.	2.458(0)
19.	1.348(3)	63.	1.342(1)	107.	2.395(0)
20.	1.100(3)	64.	1.268(1)	108.	2.334(0)
21.	9.067(2)	65.	1.200(1)	109.	2.276(0)
22.	7.544(2)	66.	1.136(1)	110.	2.221(0)
23.	6.330(2)	67.	1.078(1)	111.	2.168(0)
24.	5.352(2)	68.	1.023(1)	112.	2.117(0)
25.	4.557(2)	69.	9.716(0)	113.	2.068(0)
26.	3.905(2)	70.	9.239(0)	114.	2.021(0)
27.	3.367(2)	71.	8.794(0)	115.	1.976(0)
28.	2.919(2)	72.	8.378(0)	116.	1.933(0)
29.	2.544(2)	73.	7.988(0)	117.	1.892(0)
30.	2.229(2)	74.	7.623(0)	118.	1.852(0)
31.	1.961(2)	75.	7.281(0)	119.	1.814(0)
32.	1.732(2)	76.	6.960(0)	120.	1.778(0)
33.	1.537(2)	77.	6.659(0)	121.	1.743(0)
34.	1.369(2)	78.	6.375(0)	122.	1.709(0)
45.	1.223(2)	79.	6.109(0)	123.	1.677(0)
36.	1.097(2)	80.	5.858(0)	124.	1.645(0)
37.	9.865(1)	81.	5.621(0)	125.	1.615(0)
38.	8.901(1)	82.	5.398(0)	126.	1.587(0)
39.	8.054(1)	83.	5.187(0)	127.	1.559(0)
40.	7.308(1)	84.	4.988(0)	128.	1.532(0)
41.	6.648(1)	85.	4.800(0)	129.	1.507(0)
42.	6.063(1)	86.	4.622(0)	130.	1.482(0)
43.	5.542(1)	87.	4.454(0)	131.	1.459(0)
44.	5.078(1)	88.	4.295(0)	132.	1.436(0)

[1] H. J. Kim, W. T. Milner and F. K. McGowan, Nuclear Data *1* (1966) 203; Appendix 3.6, p. 385.

154

TABLE 12

Rutherford scattering angle (continued)

α	$\dfrac{1}{\sin^4(\frac{1}{2}\alpha)}$	α	$\dfrac{1}{\sin^4(\frac{1}{2}\alpha)}$	α	$\dfrac{1}{\sin^4(\frac{1}{2}\alpha)}$
133.	1.414(0)	149.	1.160(0)	165.	1.035(0)
134.	1.393(0)	150.	1.149(0)	166.	1.030(0)
135.	1.373(0)	151.	1.138(0)	167.	1.026(0)
136.	1.353(0)	152.	1.128(0)	168.	1.022(0)
137.	1.334(0)	153.	1.119(0)	169.	1.019(0)
138.	1.316(0)	154.	1.109(0)	170.	1.015(0)
139.	1.299(0)	155.	1.101(0)	171.	1.012(0)
140.	1.282(0)	156.	1.092(0)	172.	1.010(0)
141.	1.267(0)	157.	1.084(0)	173.	1.007(0)
142.	1.251(0)	158.	1.077(0)	174.	1.006(0)
143.	1.236(0)	159.	1.070(0)	175.	1.004(0)
144.	1.222(0)	160.	1.063(0)	176.	1.002(0)
145.	1.209(0)	161.	1.057(0)	177.	1.001(0)
146.	1.196(0)	162.	1.051(0)	178.	1.001(0)
147.	1.183(0)	163.	1.045(0)	179.	1.000(0)
148.	1.171(0)	164.	1.040(0)	180.	1.000(0)

TABLE 13

Single-particle radiation widths

It is customary to measure the strengths of electromagnetic transitions in terms of extreme single-particle units. These units are termed either Weisskopf[1] or Moszkowski[2] units; the two are the same for electric transitions, but differ for magnetic transitions. These single-particle radiation widths are given below in eV if E_γ is in MeV; the nuclear radius has been taken equal to $1.2A^{1/3} \times 10^{-13}$ cm. Wilkinson[3] has given a nomograph for the calculation of these radiation widths which allows the use of different radii.

The statistical factor S which multiplies the width has been given by Moszkowski.[2] In the table below L is the multipolarity of the transition and j_i and j_f refer to the initial and final sub-shells between which the transition takes place.

Multipole	Weisskopf units[1] (in eV)	Moszkowski units[2] (in eV)
E1	$6.8 \times 10^{-2} \; A^{2/3} E_\gamma^3 S$	
E2	$4.9 \times 10^{-8} \; A^{4/3} E_\gamma^5 S$	
E3	$2.3 \times 10^{-14} A^2 E_\gamma^7 S$	
E4	$6.8 \times 10^{-21} A^{8/3} E_\gamma^9 S$	
E5	$1.6 \times 10^{-27} A^{10/3} E_\gamma^{11} S$	
M1	$2.1 \times 10^{-2} E_\gamma^3 S$	$1.8 \times 10^{-2} E_\gamma^3 S$
M2	$1.5 \times 10^{-6} A^{2/3} E_\gamma^5 S$	$5.7 \times 10^{-8} A^{2/3} E_\gamma^5 S$
M3	$6.8 \times 10^{-15} A^{4/3} E_\gamma^7 S$	$6.2 \times 10^{-14} A^{4/3} E_\gamma^7 S$
M4	$2.1 \times 10^{-21} A^2 E_\gamma^9 S$	$3.4 \times 10^{-20} A^2 E_\gamma^9 S$
M5	$4.9 \times 10^{-28} A^{8/3} E_\gamma^{11} S$	$1.1 \times 10^{-26} A^{8/3} E_\gamma^{11} S$

$S(j_i, L, j_f)$ for $L = |j_i - j_f|$

j_f \ j_i	1/2	3/2	5/2	7/2	9/2	11/2	13/2
1/2	1	1	1	1	1	1	1
3/2	2	—	6/5	9/7	4/3	15/11	18/13
5/2	3	9/5	—	9/7	10/7	50/33	225/143
7/2	4	18/7	12/7	—	4/3	50/33	700/429
9/2	5	10/3	50/21	5/3	—	15/11	225/143
11/2	6	45/11	25/33	25/11	18/11	—	18/13
13/2	7	63/13	525/143	1225/429	315/143	21/13	—

[1] V. F. Weisskopf, Phys. Rev. *83* (1951) 1073.

[2] S. A. Moszkowski, in *Alpha-, Beta- and Gamma-Ray Spectroscopy*, ed. K. Siegbahn, Vol. 2 (North-Holland, Amsterdam, 1965) p. 863.

[3] D. H. Wilkinson, in *Nuclear Spectroscopy*, ed. F. Ajzenberg-Selove, Part B (Academic Press, New York, 1960) p. 852.

TABLE 14

Listed below are the mass excesses (in keV) and the atomic masses (in amu) for all nuclei up to $Z = 45$. The values are taken from the least-squares adjustment of 1964 made by Mattauch et al.[1]

The numbers in parentheses indicate the uncertainties in the values listed; in the Mass excess column, the decimal is given, but in the Mass column the uncertainty is given for the last figure or figures. For example, $5.012\,296\,6(203) = 5.012\,296\,6 \pm 0.000\,020\,3$. All values are based on $C^{12} \equiv 12$.

Nucleus	Mass excess (keV)		Mass (amu)		Nucleus	Mass excess (keV)		Mass (amu)	
n^1	8 071.44	(0.1)	1.008 665 2	(1)	O^{14}	8 008.00	(0.4)	14.008 597 0	(4)
					O^{15}	2 859.90	(1.2)	15.003 070 2	(12)
H^1	7 288.99	(0.1)	1.007 825 2	(1)	O^{16}	−4 736.55	(0.3)	15.994 915 0	(2)
D^2	13 135.91	(0.1)	2.014 102 2	(1)	O^{17}	− 807.70	(0.9)	16.999 132 9	(9)
T^3	14 949.95	(0.2)	3.016 049 7	(2)	O^{18}	− 782.43	(0.3)	17.999 159 8	(3)
H^4	28 220.00	(1 700.0)	4.030 295 9	(18 250)	O^{19}	3 332.70	(2.9)	19.003 577 7	(31)
H^5	31 090.00	(1 500.0)	5.033 377 1	(16 103)	O^{20}	3 799.00	(8.0)	20.004 078 4	(85)
He^3	14 931.34	(0.2)	3.016 029 7	(2)	F^{16}	10 904.00	(12.0)	16.011 706 1	(128)
He^4	2 424.75	(0.4)	4.002 603 1	(4)	F^{17}	1 951.90	(0.5)	17.002 095 5	(5)
He^5	11 454.00	(19.0)	5.012 296 6	(203)	F^{18}	872.40	(0.8)	18.000 936 5	(8)
He^6	17 598.20	(4.0)	6.018 892 8	(42)	F^{19}	−1 486.00	(0.8)	18.998 404 5	(8)
He^8	32 000.00	(2 000.0)	8.034 354 0	(21 471)	F^{20}	−11.90	(4.7)	19.999 987 1	(50)
					F^{21}	−46.00	(7.0)	20.999 950 4	(75)
Li^5	11 679.00	(37.0)	5.012 538 1	(397)					
Li^6	14 088.40	(1.1)	6.015 124 7	(11)	Ne^{18}	5 319.30	(4.7)	18.005 710 6	(50)
Li^7	14 907.30	(1.1)	7.016 003 9	(11)	Ne^{19}	1 752.00	(1.6)	19.001 880 6	(17)
Li^8	20 946.20	(1.5)	8.022 487 0	(16)	Ne^{20}	−7 041.50	(0.5)	19.992 440 5	(5)
Li^9	24 965.00	(20.0)	9.026 801 5	(214)	Ne^{21}	−5 729.90	(1.5)	20.993 848 6	(16)
					Ne^{22}	−8 024.90	(0.6)	21.991 384 7	(6)
Be^6	18 366.00	(12.0)	6.019 717 0	(128)	Ne^{23}	−5 148.30	(3.4)	22.994 472 7	(36)
Be^7	15 768.90	(1.1)	7.016 928 9	(11)	Ne^{24}	−5 949.00	(10.0)	23.993 613 2	(107)
Be^8	4 944.20	(0.8)	8.005 307 8	(8)					
Be^9	11 350.50	(0.9)	9.012 185 5	(9)	Na^{20}	8 280.00	(300.0)	20.008 889 0	(3 220)
Be^{10}	12 607.00	(2.2)	10.013 534 3	(23)	Na^{21}	−2 185.00	(8.0)	20.997 654 2	(85)
Be^{11}	20 181.00	(15.0)	11.021 665 5	(161)	Na^{22}	−5 182.20	(2.7)	21.994 436 5	(28)
					Na^{23}	−9 528.30	(1.9)	22.989 770 7	(20)
B^8	22 923.10	(1.5)	8.024 609 3	(16)	Na^{24}	−8 418.40	(3.2)	23.990 962 3	(34)
B^9	12 418.60	(1.3)	9.013 332 1	(13)	Na^{25}	−9 356.00	(9.0)	24.989 955 7	(96)
B^{10}	12 052.20	(0.5)	10.012 938 7	(5)	Na^{26}	−7 690.00	(300.0)	25.991 744 3	(3 220)
B^{11}	8 667.68	(0.3)	11.009 305 2	(3)					
B^{12}	13 370.20	(1.3)	12.014 353 6	(13)	Mg^{22}	− 140.00	(80.0)	21.999 849 6	(858)
B^{13}	16 561.60	(4.0)	13.017 779 8	(42)	Mg^{23}	−5 472.40	(2.9)	22.994 124 9	(31)
					Mg^{24}	−13 933.30	(1.7)	23.985 041 6	(18)
C^{10}	15 658.00	(13.0)	10.016 809 8	(139)	Mg^{25}	−13 190.70	(1.9)	24.985 838 9	(20)
C^{11}	10 648.40	(1.1)	11.011 431 7	(11)	Mg^{26}	−16 214.20	(1.8)	25.982 592 8	(19)
C^{12}	0.	(0)	12.000 000 0	(0)	Mg^{27}	−14 582.60	(3.8)	26.984 344 5	(40)
C^{13}	3 124.60	(0.8)	13.003 354 4	(8)	Mg^{28}	−15 020.00	(6.0)	27.983 875 0	(64)
C^{14}	3 019.82	(0.3)	14.003 241 9	(3)					
C^{15}	9 873.20	(0.9)	15.010 599 5	(9)	Al^{24}	100.00	(90.0)	24.000 107 3	(966)
C^{16}	13 693.00	(16.0)	16.014 700 2	(171)	Al^{25}	−8 931.00	(6.0)	24.990 412 0	(64)
					Al^{26}	−12 210.80	(2.3)	25.986 890 8	(24)
N^{12}	17 364.00	(7.0)	12.018 641 2	(75)	Al^{27}	−17 196.10	(1.8)	26.981 538 8	(19)
N^{13}	5 345.20	(1.1)	13.005 738 4	(11)	Al^{28}	−16 855.40	(3.7)	27.981 904 5	(39)
N^{14}	2 863.73	(0.2)	14.003 074 3	(1)	Al^{29}	−18 218.00	(6.0)	28.980 441 8	(64)
N^{15}	100.40	(0.8)	15.000 107 8	(8)	Al^{30}	−17 150.00	(250.0)	29.981 588 4	(2 683)
N^{16}	5 685.10	(3.5)	16.006 103 3	(37)					
N^{17}	7 871.00	(15.0)	17.008 449 8	(161)					

[1] J. H. E. Mattauch, W. Thiele and A. H. Wapstra, Nuclear Phys. *67* (1965) 1.

Nucleus	Mass excess (keV)		Mass (amu)		Nucleus	Mass excess (keV)		Mass (amu)	
Si^{26}	− 7 132.00	(13.0)	25.992 343 2	(139)	Ca^{38}	− 21 690.00	(1000.0)	37.976 714 1	(10 735)
Si^{27}	− 12 386.00	(2.6)	26.986 702 7	(27)	Ca^{39}	− 27 300.00	(23.0)	38.970 691 7	(246)
Si^{28}	− 21 489.90	(2.8)	27.976 929 2	(30)	Ca^{40}	− 34 847.60	(3.2)	39.962 588 8	(34)
Si^{29}	− 21 893.60	(3.7)	28.976 495 7	(39)	Ca^{41}	− 35 140.00	(8.0)	40.962 274 6	(85)
Si^{30}	− 24 439.40	(3.7)	29.973 762 8	(39)	Ca^{42}	− 38 539.70	(3.5)	41.958 624 8	(37)
Si^{31}	− 22 962.00	(5.0)	30.975 348 7	(53)	Ca^{43}	− 38 395.90	(3.9)	42.958 779 3	(41)
Si^{32}	− 24 200.00	(50.0)	31.974 019 8	(536)	Ca^{44}	− 41 459.60	(4.1)	43.955 490 1	(44)
					Ca^{45}	− 40 808.50	(3.6)	44.956 189 2	(38)
P^{28}	− 7 660.00	(280.0)	27.991 776 5	(3 005)	Ca^{46}	− 43 138.00	(9.0)	45.953 688 6	(96)
P^{29}	− 16 945.00	(6.0)	28.981 808 4	(64)	Ca^{47}	− 42 347.00	(6.0)	46.954 537 4	(64)
P^{30}	− 20 197.00	(7.0)	29.978 317 0	(75)	Ca^{48}	− 44 216.00	(9.0)	47.952 531 3	(96)
P^{31}	− 24 437.60	(1.4)	30.973 764 7	(15)	Ca^{49}	− 41 288.00	(11.0)	48.955 674 6	(118)
P^{32}	− 24 302.70	(2.1)	31.973 909 4	(22)					
P^{33}	− 26 334.60	(3.4)	32.971 727 8	(36)	Sc^{40}	− 20 900.00	(200.0)	39.977 562 4	(2 147)
P^{34}	− 24 830.00	(200.0)	33.973 343 4	(2 147)	Sc^{41}	− 28 645.00	(10.0)	40.969 247 3	(107)
					Sc^{42}	− 32 141.00	(12.0)	41.965 494 2	(128)
S^{30}	− 14 090.00	(27.0)	29.984 873 3	(289)	Sc^{43}	− 36 174.00	(8.0)	42.961 164 5	(85)
S^{31}	− 18 992.00	(11.0)	30.979 610 7	(118)	Sc^{44}	− 37 813.00	(6.0)	43.959 404 9	(64)
S^{32}	− 26 012.70	(0.9)	31.972 073 6	(9)	Sc^{45}	− 41 060.60	(3.1)	44.955 918 8	(33)
S^{33}	− 26 582.60	(2.8)	32.971 461 8	(30)	Sc^{46}	− 41 755.70	(3.7)	45.955 172 5	(39)
S^{34}	− 29 933.50	(2.7)	33.967 864 0	(28)	Sc^{47}	− 44 326.30	(3.2)	46.952 412 6	(34)
S^{35}	− 28 847.10	(1.2)	34.969 030 4	(12)	Sc^{48}	− 44 505.00	(7.0)	47.952 220 9	(75)
S^{36}	− 30 655.00	(8.0)	35.967 089 7	(85)	Sc^{49}	− 46 549.00	(5.0)	48.950 026 5	(53)
S^{37}	− 27 000.00	(70.0)	36.971 013 5	(751)	Sc^{50}	− 44 960.00	(200.0)	49.951 732 2	(2 147)
S^{38}	− 26 800.00	(150.0)	37.971 228 1	(1 610)					
					Ti^{42}	− 23 378.00	(15.0)	41.974 902 2	(161)
Cl^{32}	− 12 810.00	(380.0)	31.986 247 5	(4 079)	Ti^{43}	− 29 340.00	(150.0)	42.968 501 6	(1 610)
Cl^{33}	− 21 014.00	(12.0)	32.977 439 9	(128)	Ti^{44}	− 37 658.00	(12.0)	43.959 571 4	(128)
Cl^{34}	− 24 451.00	(6.0)	33.973 750 1	(64)	Ti^{45}	− 39 002.00	(4.8)	44.958 128 5	(51)
Cl^{35}	− 29 014.50	(1.2)	34.968 851 1	(12)	Ti^{46}	− 44 122.60	(2.3)	45.952 631 5	(24)
Cl^{36}	− 29 519.60	(4.1)	35.968 308 4	(44)	Ti^{47}	− 44 926.60	(2.5)	46.951 768 4	(26)
Cl^{37}	− 31 764.80	(1.1)	36.965 898 0	(11)	Ti^{48}	− 48 483.10	(2.0)	47.947 949 9	(21)
Cl^{38}	− 29 803.00	(8.0)	37.968 004 2	(85)	Ti^{49}	− 48 557.70	(2.0)	48.947 870 3	(21)
Cl^{39}	− 29 800.00	(18.0)	38.968 007 6	(193)	Ti^{50}	− 51 430.70	(3.3)	49.944 785 6	(35)
Cl^{40}	− 27 500.00	(500.0)	39.970 476 6	(5 367)	Ti^{51}	− 49 738.00	(6.0)	50.946 602 8	(64)
					Ti^{52}	− 49 540.00	(1 000.0)	51.946 815 5	(10 735)
Ar^{34}	− 18 394.00	(1 000.0)	33.980 252 7	(10 735)					
Ar^{35}	− 23 051.00	(16.0)	34.975 253 1	(171)	V^{46}	− 37 060.00	(9.0)	45.960 213 7	(96)
Ar^{36}	− 30 231.60	(2.3)	35.967 544 1	(24)	V^{47}	− 42 010.00	(8.0)	46.954 899 3	(85)
Ar^{37}	− 30 950.90	(1.3)	36.966 772 1	(13)	V^{48}	− 44 470.00	(3.4)	47.952 258 6	(36)
Ar^{38}	− 34 718.20	(2.5)	37.962 727 5	(26)	V^{49}	− 47 950.20	(4.5)	48.948 522 1	(48)
Ar^{39}	− 33 238.00	(6.0)	38.964 316 8	(64)	V^{50}	− 49 215.80	(3.2)	49.947 163 6	(34)
Ar^{40}	− 35 038.30	(0.8)	39.962 383 7	(8)	V^{51}	− 52 198.90	(2.4)	50.943 961 1	(25)
Ar^{41}	− 33 067.40	(4.9)	40.964 500 0	(52)	V^{52}	− 51 436.00	(5.0)	51.944 779 9	(53)
Ar^{42}	− 34 420.00	(40.0)	41.963 047 5	(429)	V^{53}	− 52 180.00	(1 000.0)	52.943 981 2	(10 735)
					V^{54}	− 49 630.00	(1 000.0)	53.946 718 7	(10 735)
K^{36}	− 16 730.00	(1 000.0)	35.982 039 0	(10 735)					
K^{37}	− 24 810.00	(45.0)	36.973 364 8	(483)	Cr^{48}	− 43 070.00	(200.0)	47.953 761 6	(2 147)
K^{38}	− 28 786.00	(10.0)	37.969 096 2	(107)	Cr^{49}	− 45 390.00	(11.0)	48.951 270 6	(118)
K^{39}	− 33 803.30	(2.6)	38.963 709 8	(27)	Cr^{50}	− 50 249.00	(3.5)	49.946 054 5	(37)
K^{40}	− 33 533.30	(1·2)	39.963 999 7	(12)	Cr^{51}	− 51 447.20	(2.6)	50.944 768 0	(27)
K^{41}	− 35 552.40	(3.5)	40.961 832 0	(37)	Cr^{52}	− 55 410.70	(3.0)	51.940 513 1	(32)
K^{42}	− 35 018.00	(10.0)	41.962 405 7	(107)	Cr^{53}	− 55 280.70	(3.0)	52.940 652 4	(32)
K^{43}	− 36 579.00	(11.0)	42.960 730 1	(118)	Cr^{54}	− 56 930.50	(3.8)	53.938 881 4	(40)
K^{44}	− 35 360.00	(200.0)	43.962 038 5	(2 147)	Cr^{55}	− 55 113.00	(7.0)	54.940 832 6	(75)
K^{45}	− 36 630.00	(200.0)	44.960 675 2	(2 147)	Cr^{56}	− 55 290.00	(150.0)	55.940 642 4	(1 610)
K^{46}	− 35 340.00	(1 000.0)	45.962 060 0	(10 735)					
K^{47}	− 36 250.00	(300.0)	46.961 082 9	(3 220)					

158

Nucleus	Mass excess (keV)		Mass (amu)	
Mn⁵⁰	−42 648.00	(27.0)	49.954 214 6	(289)
Mn⁵¹	−48 260.00	(50.0)	50.948 189 7	(536)
Mn⁵²	−50 702.00	(6.0)	51.945 568 1	(64)
Mn⁵³	−54 682.00	(7.0)	52.941 295 1	(75)
Mn⁵⁴	−55 552.00	(5.0)	53.940 361 0	(53)
Mn⁵⁵	−57 704.80	(3.3)	54.938 050 3	(35)
Mn⁵⁶	−56 903.80	(4.3)	55.938 910 0	(46)
Mn⁵⁷	−57 480.00	(300.0)	56.938 291 5	(3 220)
Mn⁵⁸	−55 650.00	(1 000.0)	57.940 256 1	(10 735)
Fe⁵²	−48 328.00	(13.0)	51.948 116 8	(139)
Fe⁵³	−50 698.00	(45.0)	52.945 572 4	(483)
Fe⁵⁴	−56 245.50	(4.6)	53.939 616 7	(49)
Fe⁵⁵	−57 473.50	(3.5)	54.938 298 2	(37)
Fe⁵⁶	−60 605.40	(4.0)	55.934 936 0	(42)
Fe⁵⁷	−60 175.50	(4.2)	56.935 397 6	(45)
Fe⁵⁸	−62 146.50	(4.8)	57.933 281 4	(51)
Fe⁵⁹	−60 659.90	(4.3)	58.934 877 4	(46)
Fe⁶⁰	−61 511.00	(30.0)	59.933 963 8	(322)
Fe⁶¹	−59 130.00	(1 000.0)	60.936 520 1	(10 735)
Co⁵⁴	−47 994.00	(7.0)	53.948 475 4	(75)
Co⁵⁵	−54 014.00	(11.0)	54.942 012 3	(118)
Co⁵⁶	−56 031.00	(8.0)	55.939 847 0	(85)
Co⁵⁷	−59 338.90	(4.9)	56.936 295 5	(52)
Co⁵⁸	−59 838.00	(6.0)	57.935 760 0	(64)
Co⁵⁹	−62 232.70	(3.6)	58.933 188 9	(38)
Co⁶⁰	−61 651.30	(4.5)	59.933 813 1	(48)
Co⁶¹	−62 930.00	(40.0)	60.932 440 3	(429)
Co⁶²	−61 528.00	(40.0)	61.933 945 7	(429)
Co⁶³	−61 920.00	(200.0)	62.933 524 6	(2 147)
Ni⁵⁶	−53 918.00	(15.0)	55.942 115 3	(161)
Ni⁵⁷	−56 104.00	(16.0)	56.939 768 8	(171)
Ni⁵⁸	−60 228.00	(5.0)	57.935 341 4	(53)
Ni⁵⁹	−61 158.70	(4.1)	58.934 341 9	(44)
Ni⁶⁰	−64 470.70	(4.6)	59.930 786 6	(49)
Ni⁶¹	−64 220.00	(6.0)	60.931 055 5	(64)
Ni⁶²	−66 748.00	(5.0)	61.928 341 4	(53)
Ni⁶³	−65 516.00	(5.0)	62.929 664 1	(53)
Ni⁶⁴	−67 106.00	(5.0)	63.927 957 1	(53)
Ni⁶⁵	−65 137.00	(8.0)	64.930 070 9	(85)
Ni⁶⁶	−66 055.00	(31.0)	65.929 085 7	(332)
Cu⁵⁸	−51 659.00	(7.0)	57.944 540 5	(75)
Cu⁵⁹	−56 359.00	(21.0)	58.939 494 6	(225)
Cu⁶⁰	−58 346.00	(8.0)	59.937 361 7	(85)
Cu⁶¹	−61 984.00	(7.0)	60.933 455 9	(75)
Cu⁶²	−62 813.00	(10.0)	61.932 566 2	(107)
Cu⁶³	−65 583.10	(4.9)	62.929 592 1	(52)
Cu⁶⁴	−65 427.60	(4.8)	63.929 759 0	(51)
Cu⁶⁵	−67 266.00	(5.0)	64.927 784 9	(53)
Cu⁶⁶	−66 255.00	(9.0)	65.928 870 2	(96)
Cu⁶⁷	−67 291.00	(12.0)	66.927 758 2	(128)
Cu⁶⁸	−65 410.00	(60.0)	67.929 778 1	(644)

Nucleus	Mass excess (keV)		Mass (amu)	
Zn⁶¹	−56 580.00	(200.0)	60.939 257 6	(2 147)
Zn⁶²	−61 123.00	(13.0)	61.934 380 5	(139)
Zn⁶³	−62 217.00	(6.0)	62.933 206 1	(64)
Zn⁶⁴	−66 000.30	(4.6)	63.929 144 4	(49)
Zn⁶⁵	−65 917.00	(5.0)	64.929 233 6	(53)
Zn⁶⁶	−68 881.00	(6.0)	65.926 051 1	(64)
Zn⁶⁷	−67 863.00	(10.0)	66.927 144 1	(107)
Zn⁶⁸	−69 994.00	(5.0)	67.924 856 2	(53)
Zn⁶⁹	−68 425.00	(6.0)	68.926 541 3	(64)
Zn⁷⁰	−69 550.00	(6.0)	69.925 333 0	(64)
Zn⁷¹	−67 520.00	(50.0)	70.927 512 2	(536)
Zn⁷²	−68 144.00	(9.0)	71.926 842 7	(96)
Ga⁶³	−56 720.00	(1 000.0)	62.939 107 4	(10 735)
Ga⁶⁴	−58 928.00	(30.0)	63.936 737 1	(322)
Ga⁶⁵	−62 658.00	(16.0)	64.932 732 6	(171)
Ga⁶⁶	−63 706.00	(6.0)	65.931 607 2	(64)
Ga⁶⁷	−66 865.00	(10.0)	66.928 216 0	(107)
Ga⁶⁸	−67 074.00	(6.0)	67.927 990 9	(64)
Ga⁶⁹	−69 326.20	(3.4)	68.925 573 3	(36)
Ga⁷⁹	−68 897.00	(6.0)	69.926 034 0	(64)
Ga⁷¹	−70 134.70	(4.3)	70.924 705 5	(46)
Ga⁷²	−68 583.00	(7.0)	71.926 371 6	(75)
Ga⁷³	−69 743.00	(40.0)	72.925 126 1	(429)
Ga⁷⁴	−67 820.00	(50.0)	73.927 190 8	(536)
Ge⁶⁵	−56 260.00	(1 000.0)	64.939 600 9	(10 735)
Ge⁶⁶	−60 740.00	(150.0)	65.934 791 6	(1 610)
Ge⁶⁷	−62 460.00	(100.0)	66.932 945 3	(1 073)
Ge⁶⁸	−66 570.00	(1 000.0)	67.928 532 6	(10 735)
Ge⁶⁹	−67 100.70	(4.2)	68.927 962 3	(45)
Ge⁷⁰	−70 558.00	(1.7)	69.924 251 6	(18)
Ge⁷¹	−69 902.00	(5.0)	70.924 955 4	(53)
Ge⁷²	−72 579.10	(1.6)	71.922 081 0	(17)
Ge⁷³	−71 293.00	(1.8)	72.923 461 9	(19)
Ge⁷⁴	−73 418.50	(1.6)	73.921 179 8	(17)
Ge⁷⁵	−71 833.00	(19.0)	74.922 882 1	(203)
Ge⁷⁶	−73 209.30	(1.9)	75.921 404 8	(20)
Ge⁷⁷	−71 170.00	(50.0)	76.923 594 5	(536)
As⁶⁹	−63 200.00	(300.0)	68.932 149 9	(3 220)
As⁷⁰	−64 322.00	(30.0)	69.930 945 4	(322)
As⁷¹	−67 893.00	(9.0)	70.927 112 6	(96)
As⁷²	−68 219.00	(10.0)	71.926 762 6	(107)
As⁷³	−70 921.00	(30.0)	72.923 861 5	(322)
As⁷⁴	−70 855.00	(3.9)	73.923 932 1	(41)
As⁷⁵	−73 031.20	(3.7)	74.921 595 6	(39)
As⁷⁶	−72 286.00	(12.0)	75.922 395 7	(128)
As⁷⁷	−73 917.00	(10.0)	76.920 644 8	(107)
As⁷⁸	−72 750.00	(200.0)	77.921 897 9	(2 147)
As⁷⁹	−73 680.00	(60.0)	78.920 888 9	(644)
As⁸⁰	−71 750.00	(200.0)	79.922 971 7	(2 147)

Nucleus	Mass excess (keV)		Mass (amu)		Nucleus	Mass excess (keV)		Mass (amu)	
Se^{71}	$-63\,490.00$	(300.0)	70.931 839 0	(3 220)	Sr^{82}	$-76\,020.00$	(1 000.0)	81.918 387 4	(10 735)
Se^{72}	$-67\,620.00$	(1 000.0)	71.927 405 4	(10 735)	Sr^{83}	$-77\,120.00$	(1 410.0)	82.917 206 8	(15 137)
Se^{73}	$-68\,171.00$	(32.0)	72.926 814 1	(343)	Sr^{84}	$-80\,638.00$	(3.7)	83.913 429 3	(39)
Se^{74}	$-72\,212.20$	(4.8)	73.922 474 9	(51)	Sr^{85}	$-81\,049.00$	(30.0)	84.912 988 7	(322)
Se^{75}	$-72\,166.30$	(4.1)	74.922 524 5	(44)	Sr^{86}	$-84\,499.10$	(4.8)	85.909 284 6	(51)
Se^{76}	$-75\,257.00$	(7.0)	75.919 206 6	(75)	Sr^{87}	$-84\,864.90$	(3.3)	86.908 891 7	(35)
Se^{77}	$-74\,601.00$	(5.0)	76.919 910 4	(53)	Sr^{88}	$-87\,894.00$	(6.0)	87.905 639 6	(64)
Se^{78}	$-77\,020.50$	(2.5)	77.917 313 6	(26)	Sr^{89}	$-86\,215.00$	(7.0)	88.907 442 1	(75)
Se^{79}	$-75\,920.80$	(4.4)	78.918 494 2	(47)	Sr^{90}	$-85\,932.00$	(8.0)	89.907 746 3	(85)
Se^{80}	$-77\,753.00$	(2.7)	79.916 526 8	(28)	Sr^{91}	$-83\,683.00$	(15.0)	90.910 161 0	(161)
Se^{81}	$-76\,396.00$	(7.0)	80.917 984 0	(75)	Sr^{92}	$-82\,920.00$	(70.0)	91.910 979 3	(751)
Se^{82}	$-77\,586.00$	(6.0)	81.916 706 1	(64)	Sr^{92}	$-79\,450.00$	(100.0)	92.914 705 3	(1 073)
					Sr^{94}	$-78\,820.00$	(220.0)	93.915 381 4	(2 361)
Br^{73}	$-63\,470.00$	(1 000.0)	72.931 860 9	(10 735)					
Br^{74}	$-65\,410.00$	(1 000.0)	73.929 778 1	(10 735)	Y^{84}	$-74\,340.00$	(100.0)	83.920 190 8	(1 073)
Br^{75}	$-69\,444.00$	(20.0)	74.925 447 5	(214)	Y^{85}	$-77\,789.00$	(32.0)	84.916 487 7	(343)
Br^{76}	$-70\,630.00$	(60.0)	75.924 173 4	(644)	Y^{86}	$-79\,226.00$	(17.0)	85.914 945 6	(182)
Br^{77}	$-73\,236.00$	(6.0)	76.921 376 2	(64)	Y^{87}	$-83\,150.00$	(200.0)	86.910 733 2	(2 147)
Br^{78}	$-73\,447.00$	(6.0)	77.921 149 3	(64)	Y^{88}	$-84\,273.00$	(7.0)	87.909 526 8	(75)
Br^{79}	$-76\,074.70$	(3.1)	78.918 328 3	(33)	Y^{89}	$-87\,678.30$	(4.5)	88.905 871 4	(48)
Br^{80}	$-75\,882.20$	(3.4)	79.918 535 2	(36)	Y^{90}	$-86\,476.00$	(7.0)	89.907 116 7	(75)
Br^{81}	$-77\,972.00$	(5.0)	80.916 291 2	(53)	Y^{91}	$-86\,353.00$	(11.0)	90.907 294 3	(118)
Br^{82}	$-77\,497.00$	(5.0)	81.916 801 5	(13)	Y^{92}	$-84\,834.00$	(20.0)	91.908 925 1	(214)
Br^{83}	$-79\,019.00$	(16.0)	82.915 167 8	(171)	Y^{93}	$-84\,250.00$	(21.0)	92.909 551 6	(225)
Br^{84}	$-77\,730.00$	(50.0)	83.916 551 6	(536)	Y^{94}	$-82\,270.00$	(200.0)	93.911 677 4	(2 147)
Br^{85}	$-78\,680.00$	(100.0)	84.915 531 2	(1 073)	Y^{95}	$-81\,460.00$	(1 000.0)	94.912 547 1	(10 735)
Br^{86}	$-76\,200.00$	(500.0)	85.918 193 8	(5 367)	Y^{96}	$-78\,530.00$	(1 000.0)	95.915 692 3	(10 735)
Kr^{74}	$-62\,310.00$	(1 410.0)	73.933 105 5	(15 137)	Zr^{86}	$-78\,030.00$	(1 000.0)	85.916 229 2	(10 735)
Kr^{75}	$-64\,340.00$	(1 000.0)	74.930 926 3	(10 735)	Zr^{87}	$-79\,650.00$	(200.0)	86.914 490 7	(2 147)
Kr^{76}	$-69\,430.00$	(1 000.0)	75.925 461 8	(10 735)	Zr^{88}	$-83\,770.00$	(1 000.0)	87.910 067 6	(10 735)
Kr^{77}	$-70\,350.00$	(80.0)	76.924 474 7	(858)	Zr^{89}	$-84\,845.00$	(5.0)	88.908 912 7	(53)
Kr^{78}	$-74\,143.00$	(5.0)	77.920 402 5	(53)	Zr^{90}	$-88\,770.20$	(3.9)	89.904 699 3	(41)
Kr^{79}	$-74\,455.00$	(6.0)	78.920 067 8	(64)	Zr^{91}	$-87\,892.80$	(4.8)	90.905 641 6	(51)
Kr^{80}	$-77\,891.00$	(6.0)	79.916 379 0	(64)	Zr^{92}	$-88\,461.70$	(3.3)	91.905 030 3	(35)
Kr^{81}	$-77\,670.00$	(100.0)	80.916 615 5	(1 073)	Zr^{93}	$-87\,140.00$	(5.0)	92.906 449 3	(53)
Kr^{82}	$-80\,589.40$	(4.7)	81.913 481 7	(50)	Zr^{94}	$-87\,267.00$	(3.4)	93.906 312 9	(36)
Kr^{83}	$-79\,984.70$	(4.4)	82.914 131 2	(47)	Zr^{95}	$-85\,633.10$	(4.9)	94.908 035 3	(52)
Kr^{84}	$-82\,432.60$	(3.3)	83.911 502 8	(35)	Zr^{96}	$-85\,429.80$	(4.7)	95.908 285 1	(50)
Kr^{85}	$-81\,483.00$	(6.0)	84.912 522 3	(64)	Zr^{97}	$-82\,934.00$	(22.0)	96.910 965 0	(236)
Kr^{86}	$-83\,259.30$	(4.0)	85.910 615 9	(42)	Zr^{98}	$-82\,010.00$	(1 410.0)	97.911 956 8	(15 137)
Kr^{87}	$-80\,698.00$	(9.0)	86.913 365 4	(96)					
Kr^{88}	$-79\,850.00$	(220.0)	87.914 275 2	(2 361)	Nb^{88}	$-76\,570.00$	(1 410.0)	87.917 797 1	(15 137)
Kr^{89}	$-77\,700.00$	(500.0)	88.916 584 0	(5 367)	Nb^{89}	$-80\,960.00$	(90.0)	88.913 084 0	(966)
Kr^{90}	$-74\,780.00$	(100.0)	89.919 718 7	(1 073)	Nb^{90}	$-82\,660.00$	(11.0)	89.911 258 7	(118)
					Nb^{91}	$-86\,750.00$	(60.0)	90.906 868 0	(644)
Rb^{80}	$-72\,800.00$	(600.0)	79.921 844 5	(6 441)	Nb^{92}	$-86\,431.00$	(9.0)	91.907 210 4	(96)
Rb^{81}	$-75\,430.00$	(100.0)	80.919 020 7	(1 073)	Nb^{93}	$-87\,203.50$	(4.7)	92.906 380 7	(50)
Rb^{82}	$-76\,419.00$	(30.0)	81.917 959 2	(322)	Nb^{94}	$-86\,346.00$	(14.0)	93.907 301 9	(150)
Rb^{83}	$-79\,420.00$	(1 000.0)	82.914 736 7	(10 735)	Nb^{95}	$-86\,784.10$	(3.1)	94.906 831 7	(33)
Rb^{84}	$-79\,752.50$	(4.3)	83.914 380 1	(46)	Nb^{96}	$-85\,644.00$	(25.0)	95.908 055 3	(268)
Rb^{85}	$-82\,156.00$	(5.0)	84.911 800 4	(53)	Nb^{97}	$-85\,606.00$	(7.0)	96.908 096 3	(75)
Rb^{86}	$-82\,722.00$	(7.0)	85.911 191 9	(75)	Nb^{98}	$-83\,510.00$	(1 000.0)	97.910 346 0	(10 735)
Rb^{87}	$-84\,590.80$	(3.1)	86.909 186 4	(33)	Nb^{99}	$-82\,860.00$	(1 000.0)	98.911 044 1	(10 735)
Rb^{88}	$-82\,650.00$	(90.0)	87.911 269 2	(966)	Nb^{100}	$-80\,090.00$	(1 000.0)	99.914 017 7	(10 735)
Rb^{89}	$-82\,300.00$	(50.0)	88.911 644 9	(536)					
Rb^{90}	$-79\,340.00$	(100.0)	89.914 823 5	(1 073)					
Rb^{91}	$-78\,180.00$	(1 000.0)	90.916 068 1	(10 735)					
Rb^{92}	$-75\,320.00$	(1 000.0)	91.919 138 9	(10 735)					

Nucleus	Mass excess (keV)		Mass (amu)		Nucleus	Mass excess (keV)		Mass (amu)	
Mo⁹⁰	−80 160.00	(100.0)	89.913 942 3	(1 073)	Ru⁹⁵	−84 018.00	(37.0)	94.909 800 5	(397)
Mo⁹¹	−82 290.00	(50.0)	90.911 656 4	(536)	Ru⁹⁶	−86 071.00	(5.0)	95.907 596 6	(53)
Mo⁹²	−86 804.30	(3.2)	91.906 809 8	(34)	Ru⁹⁷	−86 040.00	(1 410.0)	96.907 630 0	(15 137)
Mo⁹³	−86 785.00	(13.0)	92.906 830 8	(139)	Ru⁹⁸	−88 221.50	(4.1)	97.905 287 7	(44)
Mo⁹⁴	−88 406.50	(2.7)	93.905 089 4	(28)	Ru⁹⁹	−87 619.00	(4.0)	98.905 935 3	(42)
Mo⁹⁵	−87 708.90	(3.0)	94.905 839 0	(32)	Ru¹⁰⁰	−89 218.70	(4.8)	99.904 217 7	(51)
Mo⁹⁶	−88 794.20	(2.5)	95.904 673 6	(26)	Ru¹⁰¹	−87 953.20	(3.1)	100.905 576 7	(33)
Mo⁹⁷	−87 538.90	(2.7)	96.906 021 1	(28)	Ru¹⁰²	−89 097.90	(4.4)	101.904 347 4	(47)
Mo⁹⁸	−88 109.70	(2.7)	97.905 407 9	(28)	Ru¹⁰³	−87 274.00	(19.0)	102.906 305 3	(203)
Mo⁹⁹	−85 957.00	(9.0)	98.907 719 6	(96)	Ru¹⁰⁴	−88 089.90	(4.8)	103.905 429 8	(51)
Mo¹⁰⁰	−86 185.30	(3.5)	99.907 474 5	(37)	Ru¹⁰⁵	−85 995.00	(16.0)	104.907 678 6	(171)
Mo¹⁰¹	−83 504.00	(19.0)	100.910 352 7	(203)	Ru¹⁰⁶	−86 328.00	(11.0)	105.907 321 0	(118)
Mo¹⁰²	−83 600.00	(1 410.0)	101.910 249 7	(15 137)	Ru¹⁰⁷	−83 710.00	(300.0)	106.910 131 5	(3 220)
					Ru¹⁰⁸	−83 700.00	(600.0)	107.910 141 9	(6 441)
Tc⁹²	−78 750.00	(140.0)	91.915 456 8	(1 502)	Rh⁹⁷	−82 550.00	(1 410.0)	96.911 377 0	(15 137)
Tc⁹³	−83 599.00	(19.0)	92.910 250 7	(203)	Rh⁹⁸	−84 020.00	(300.0)	97.909 798 6	(3 220)
Tc⁹⁴	−84 146.00	(7.0)	93.909 663 2	(75)	Rh⁹⁹	−85 519.00	(20.0)	98.908 189 8	(214)
Tc⁹⁵	−86 050.00	(21.0)	94.907 619 5	(225)	Rh¹⁰⁰	−85 579.00	(21.0)	99.908 124 9	(225)
Tc⁹⁶	−85 860.00	(50.0)	95.907 823 6	(536)	Rh¹⁰¹	−87 393.00	(18.0)	100.906 177 5	(193)
Tc⁹⁷	−87 240.00	(1 000.0)	96.906 341 6	(10 735)	Rh¹⁰²	−86 774.00	(8.0)	101.906 842 2	(85)
Tc⁹⁸	−86 520.00	(200.0)	97.907 115 0	(2 147)	Rh¹⁰³	−88 014.40	(4.5)	102.905 510 9	(48)
Tc⁹⁹	−87 327.00	(5.0)	98.906 248 1	(53)	Rh¹⁰⁴	−86 945.00	(6.0)	103.906 658 2	(64)
Tc¹⁰⁰	−85 850.00	(60.0)	99.907 834 1	(644)	Rh¹⁰⁵	−87 866.00	(12.0)	104.905 670 2	(128)
Tc¹⁰¹	−86 324.00	(25.0)	100.907 325 7	(268)	Rh¹⁰⁶	−86 367.00	(11.0)	105.907 279 0	(118)
Tc¹⁰²	−84 600.00	(1 000.0)	101.909 175 9	(10 735)	Rh¹⁰⁷	−86 858.00	(40.0)	106.906 751 6	(429)
Tc¹⁰³	−84 920.00	(100.0)	102.908 832 6	(1 073)	Rh¹⁰⁸	−85 000.00	(600.0)	107.908 746 7	(6 441)
Tc¹⁰⁴	−82 240.00	(100.0)	103.911 709 8	(1 073)	Rh¹⁰⁹	−85 100.00	(1 000.0)	108.908 639 0	(10 735)
Tc¹⁰⁵	−82 590.00	(200.0)	104.911 334 0	(2 147)	Rh¹¹⁰	−82 800.00	(500.0)	109.911 109 0	(5 367)

TABLE 15

Spherical harmonics, $Y_l^m(\theta, \phi)$

$Y_0^0(\theta, \phi) = 1/(4\pi)^{\frac{1}{2}}$

$Y_1^0(\theta, \phi) = (3/4\pi)^{\frac{1}{2}} \cos \theta$

$Y_1^{\pm 1}(\theta, \phi) = \mp (3/8\pi)^{\frac{1}{2}} \sin \theta \, e^{\pm i\phi}$

$Y_2^0(\theta, \phi) = (5/16\pi)^{\frac{1}{2}} (2 \cos^2 \theta - \sin^2 \theta)$

$Y_2^{\pm 1}(\theta, \phi) = \mp (15/8\pi)^{\frac{1}{2}} \cos \theta \sin \theta \, e^{\pm i\phi}$

$Y_2^{\pm 2}(\theta, \phi) = (15/32\pi)^{\frac{1}{2}} \sin^2 \theta \, e^{\pm 2i\phi}$

$Y_3^0(\theta, \phi) = (7/16\pi)^{\frac{1}{2}} (2 \cos^3 \theta - 3 \cos \theta \sin^2 \theta)$

$Y_3^{\pm 1}(\theta, \phi) = \mp (21/64\pi)^{\frac{1}{2}} (4 \cos^2 \theta \sin \theta - \sin^3 \theta) e^{\pm i\phi}$

$Y_3^{\pm 2}(\theta, \phi) = (105/32\pi)^{\frac{1}{2}} \cos \theta \sin^2 \theta \, e^{\pm 2i\phi}$

$Y_3^{\pm 3}(\theta, \phi) = \mp (35/64\pi)^{\frac{1}{2}} \sin^3 \theta \, e^{\pm 3i\phi}$

$$Y_l^m(\theta, \phi) = \frac{(-1)^{l+m}}{2^l l!} \left[\frac{(2l+1)(l-m)!}{4\pi(l+m)!} \right]^{\frac{1}{2}} (\sin \theta)^m \left[\frac{\partial}{\partial(\cos \theta)} \right]^{l+m} (\sin \theta)^{2l} \exp(im\phi)$$

TABLE 16

Legendre polynomials, $P_n(x)$

$P_0(x) = 1$

$P_1(x) = \cos\theta = x$

$P_2(x) = \frac{1}{4}(3\cos 2\theta + 1) = \frac{1}{2}(3x^2 - 1)$

$P_3(x) = \frac{1}{8}(5\cos 3\theta + 3\cos\theta) = \frac{1}{2}(5x^3 - 3x)$

$P_4(x) = \frac{1}{64}(35\cos 4\theta + 20\cos 2\theta + 9)$

$\qquad = \frac{1}{8}(35x^4 - 30x^2 + 3)$

$P_5(x) = \frac{1}{128}(63\cos 5\theta + 35\cos 3\theta + 30\cos\theta)$

$\qquad = \frac{1}{8}(63x^5 - 70x^3 + 15x)$

$P_6(x) = \frac{1}{512}(231\cos 6\theta + 126\cos 4\theta + 105\cos 2\theta + 50)$

$\qquad = \frac{1}{16}(231x^6 - 315x^4 + 105x^2 - 5)$

$P_n(x) = \frac{1}{2^n n!}\,\frac{d^n}{dx^n}(x^2 - 1)^n$

Zeros of the Legendre polynomials

$l = 0$: None

$l = 1$: $x = 0$; $\theta = 90°$

$l = 2$: $x = \pm 0.577\,35$; $\theta = 54.736°,\ 125.264°$

$l = 3$: $x = 0,\ \pm 0.774\,60$; $\theta = 39.231°,\ 90°,\ 140.769°$

$l = 4$: $x = \pm 0.339\,98,\ \pm 0.861\,14$;

$\qquad \theta = 30.556°,\ 70.124°,\ 109.876°,\ 149.444°$

$l = 5$: $x = 0,\ \pm 0.538\,47,\ \pm 0.906\,18$

$\qquad \theta = 25.983°,\ 57.421°,\ 90°,\ 122.579°,\ 154.017°$

$l = 6$: $x = \pm 0.238\,62,\ \pm 0.661\,21,\ \pm 0.932\,47$;

$\qquad \theta = 21.177°,\ 48.608°,\ 76.195°,\ 103.805°,\ 131.392°,\ 157.823°$

TABLE 17
Numerical constants

π	$= 3.141\,593$	$4\pi^2$	$= 39.478\,418$
2π	$= 6.283\,185$	$1/\pi^2$	$= 0.101\,321$
3π	$= 9.424\,778$	$1/2\pi^2$	$= 0.050\,661$
4π	$= 12.566\,371$	$1/4\pi^2$	$= 0.025\,330$
$\pi/2$	$= 1.570\,796$	$\sqrt{\pi}$	$= 1.772\,454$
$\pi/3$	$= 1.047\,198$	$\sqrt{\pi/4}$	$= 0.886\,227$
$\pi/4$	$= 0.785\,398$	$\sqrt{\pi}/4$	$= 0.443\,114$
$2\pi/3$	$= 2.094\,395$	$\sqrt{\pi/2}$	$= 1.253\,314$
$4\pi/3$	$= 4.188\,790$	$\sqrt{2/\pi}$	$= 0.797\,885$
$1/\pi$	$= 0.318\,310$	π^3	$= 31.006\,277$
$2/\pi$	$= 0.636\,620$	$(\pi)^{\frac{1}{3}}$	$= 1.464\,592$
$4/\pi$	$= 1.273\,240$	$(\pi)^{-\frac{1}{3}}$	$= 0.682\,784$
$1/2\pi$	$= 0.159\,155$	$(\pi)^{\frac{1}{4}}$	$= 2.145\,029$
$1/4\pi$	$= 0.079\,578$	$1/\sqrt{\pi}$	$= 0.564\,190$
π^2	$= 9.869\,604$	$1/\sqrt{2\pi}$	$= 0.398\,942$
$2\pi^2$	$= 19.739\,209$	$2/\sqrt{\pi}$	$= 1.128\,379$
e	$= 2.718\,282$	$1/e$	$= 0.367\,879$
$\log_{10}e$	$= 0.434\,294$	$\log_e 10$	$= 2.302\,585$
$\log_e 2$	$= 0.693\,147$	Euler constant:	
		$\gamma =$	$0.577\,216$

TABLE 18

Values of exp(−x) for $0 \leqq x \leqq 30.9$

The numbers in parentheses are the powers of ten by which the preceding numbers are to be multiplied.

x	0	0.1	0.2	0.3	0.4	0.5	0.6	0.7	0.8	0.9
0	1.000(0)	9.048(−1)	8.187(−1)	7.408(−1)	6.703(−1)	6.065(−1)	5.488(−1)	4.966(−1)	4.493(−1)	4.066(−1)
1	3.679(−1)	3.329(−1)	3.012(−1)	2.725(−1)	2.466(−1)	2.231(−1)	2.019(−1)	1.827(−1)	1.653(−1)	1.496(−1)
2	1.353(−1)	1.225(−1)	1.108(−1)	1.003(−1)	9.072(−2)	8.209(−2)	7.427(−2)	6.721(−2)	6.081(−2)	5.502(−2)
3	4.979(−2)	4.505(−2)	4.076(−2)	3.688(−2)	3.337(−2)	3.020(−2)	2.732(−2)	2.472(−2)	2.237(−2)	2.024(−2)
4	1.832(−2)	1.657(−2)	1.500(−2)	1.357(−2)	1.228(−2)	1.111(−2)	1.005(−2)	9.095(−3)	8.230(−3)	7.447(−3)
5	6.738(−3)	6.097(−3)	5.517(−3)	4.992(−3)	4.517(−3)	4.087(−3)	3.698(−3)	3.346(−3)	3.028(−3)	2.739(−3)
6	2.479(−3)	2.243(−3)	2.029(−3)	1.836(−3)	1.662(−3)	1.503(−3)	1.360(−3)	1.231(−3)	1.114(−3)	1.008(−3)
7	9.119(−4)	8.251(−4)	7.466(−4)	6.755(−4)	6.113(−4)	5.531(−4)	5.005(−4)	4.528(−4)	4.097(−4)	3.707(−4)
8	3.355(−4)	3.035(−4)	2.747(−4)	2.485(−4)	2.249(−4)	2.035(−4)	1.841(−4)	1.666(−4)	1.507(−4)	1.364(−4)
9	1.234(−4)	1.117(−4)	1.010(−4)	9.142(−5)	8.272(−5)	7.485(−5)	6.773(−5)	6.128(−5)	5.545(−5)	5.017(−5)
10	4.540(−5)	4.108(−5)	3.717(−5)	3.363(−5)	3.043(−5)	2.754(−5)	2.492(−5)	2.254(−5)	2.040(−5)	1.846(−5)
11	1.670(−5)	1.511(−5)	1.367(−5)	1.237(−5)	1.120(−5)	1.013(−5)	9.166(−6)	8.294(−6)	7.505(−6)	6.790(−6)
12	6.144(−6)	5.560(−6)	5.030(−6)	4.552(−6)	4.119(−6)	3.727(−6)	3.372(−6)	3.051(−6)	2.761(−6)	2.498(−6)
13	2.260(−6)	2.045(−6)	1.851(−6)	1.674(−6)	1.515(−6)	1.371(−6)	1.240(−6)	1.122(−6)	1.016(−6)	9.190(−7)
14	8.315(−7)	7.524(−7)	6.808(−7)	6.160(−7)	5.574(−7)	5.043(−7)	4.564(−7)	4.129(−7)	3.736(−7)	3.381(−7)
15	3.059(−7)	2.768(−7)	2.505(−7)	2.266(−7)	2.051(−7)	1.855(−7)	1.679(−7)	1.519(−7)	1.375(−7)	1.244(−7)
16	1.125(−7)	1.018(−7)	9.214(−8)	8.337(−8)	7.543(−8)	6.826(−8)	6.176(−8)	5.588(−8)	5.057(−8)	4.575(−8)
17	4.140(−8)	3.746(−8)	3.389(−8)	3.067(−8)	2.775(−8)	2.511(−8)	2.272(−8)	2.056(−8)	1.860(−8)	1.683(−8)
18	1.523(−8)	1.378(−8)	1.247(−8)	1.128(−8)	1.021(−8)	9.237(−9)	8.358(−9)	7.563(−9)	6.843(−9)	6.192(−9)
19	5.603(−9)	5.070(−9)	4.587(−9)	4.151(−9)	3.756(−9)	3.398(−9)	3.075(−9)	2.782(−9)	2.518(−9)	2.278(−9)
20	2.061(−9)	1.865(−9)	1.688(−9)	1.527(−9)	1.382(−9)	1.250(−9)	1.131(−9)	1.024(−9)	9.261(−10)	8.380(−10)
21	7.583(−10)	6.861(−10)	6.208(−10)	5.617(−10)	5.083(−10)	4.599(−10)	4.161(−10)	3.765(−10)	3.407(−10)	3.083(−10)
22	2.789(−10)	2.524(−10)	2.284(−10)	2.066(−10)	1.870(−10)	1.692(−10)	1.531(−10)	1.385(−10)	1.253(−10)	1.134(−10)
23	1.026(−10)	9.285(−11)	8.402(−11)	7.602(−11)	6.879(−11)	6.224(−11)	5.632(−11)	5.096(−11)	4.611(−11)	4.172(−11)
24	3.775(−11)	3.416(−11)	3.091(−11)	2.797(−11)	2.531(−11)	2.290(−11)	2.072(−11)	1.875(−11)	1.696(−11)	1.535(−11)
25	1.389(−11)	1.257(−11)	1.137(−11)	1.029(−11)	9.309(−12)	8.423(−12)	7.622(−12)	6.987(−12)	6.240(−12)	5.646(−12)
26	5.109(−12)	4.623(−12)	4.183(−12)	3.785(−12)	3.425(−12)	3.099(−12)	2.804(−12)	2.537(−12)	2.296(−12)	2.077(−12)
27	1.880(−12)	1.701(−12)	1.539(−12)	1.392(−12)	1.260(−12)	1.140(−12)	1.032(−12)	9.333(−13)	8.445(−13)	7.642(−13)
28	6.914(−13)	6.256(−13)	5.661(−13)	5.122(−13)	4.635(−13)	4.194(−13)	3.795(−13)	3.434(−13)	3.107(−13)	2.811(−13)
29	2.544(−13)	2.302(−13)	2.083(−13)	1.884(−13)	1.705(−13)	1.543(−13)	1.396(−13)	1.263(−13)	1.143(−13)	1.034(−13)
30	9.358(−14)	8.467(−14)	7.661(−14)	6.932(−14)	6.273(−14)	5.676(−14)	5.136(−14)	4.647(−14)	4.205(−14)	3.805(−14)

C. USEFUL EQUATIONS AND FORMULAS

1. Particle energies in electrostatic analyzers

The relativistic relationship between the energy E of a particle traversing a cylindrical electrostatic analyzer of uniform plate separation d and with voltage V across the plates is:

$$E \cong (ZeV\varrho/2d)[1+d^2/24\varrho^2]^{-1}[1+E/2E_0]$$

where $\varrho = (\varrho_{inner}\varrho_{outer})^{\frac{1}{2}}$ is the geometric mean radius of the analyzer, and where E_0 and Z are the rest energy and the charge of the particle, respectively.

2. Particle energies in magnetic analyzers

If a charged-particle beam is analyzed in a uniform-field magnet, and if the magnetic field is measured with a nuclear resonance device, then the relativistic relationship between the energy E of the particle and the resonance frequency f is:

$$E \cong kf^2[Z^2/(M_0/M_p)][1-E/2E_0]$$

where k is the "calibration constant" of the analyzer (and may be a weak function of the magnetic field because of saturation and fringing field effects), Z is the charge of the particle analyzed, and M_0 and E_0 are the particle's rest mass and rest energy, respectively. Since it is assumed that the primary calibration is in terms of proton energies, M_p (the proton rest mass) has been introduced for convenience. In the table below, F is the fraction of the total kinetic energy of the diatomic or triatomic ion which a single proton, deuteron, or triton has (neglecting internal motion of the ion).

Particle type	$Z^2/(M_0/M_p)$	E_0(MeV)	F
H^+	1.000 000	938.256	
H_2^+	0.499 864	1 877.023	0.499 864
H_3^+	0.333 212	2 815.790	0.333 212
D^+	0.500 248	1 875.581	
D_2^+	0.250 090	3 751.673	0.499 932
D_3^+	0.166 719	5 627.765	0.333 273
T^+	0.334 033	2 808.873	
T_2^+	0.167 001	5 618.257	0.499 955
T_3^+	0.111 331	8 427.641	0.333 293
He^{3+}	0.334 035	2 808.854	
He^{3++}	1.336 384	2 808.343	
He^{4+}	0.251 690	3 727.826	
He^{4++}	1.006 896	3 727.315	

3. The normal or Gaussian distribution

The normal or Gaussian distribution is defined by the following expression:

$$dP_x = (1/\sigma\sqrt{2\pi})\exp[-(x-x_0)^2/2\sigma^2]\,dx$$

where x_0 is the mean value of x and σ is the standard deviation. The distribution is normalized:

$$\int_{-\infty}^{+\infty} dP_x = 1.$$

Maximum slope $= 1/\sigma^2\sqrt{2\pi e} = 0.242/\sigma^2$.
Maximum slope occurs at $(x-x_0) = \pm\sigma$.
Value of y at maximum slope $= y_\sigma = y(x-x_0 = \pm\sigma) = 1/\sigma\sqrt{2\pi e} = 0.242/\sigma$.
Tangents to the distribution curve at the positions of maximum slope intercept the x-axis at $(x-x_0) = \pm 2\sigma$.
Maximum of distribution: $y_{max} = 1/\sigma\sqrt{2\pi}$.
$y_\sigma/y_{max} = e^{-\frac{1}{2}} = 0.6065$.
Half width $= \sigma\sqrt{2\ln 2} = 1.177\,\sigma$ at $y = \frac{1}{2}y_{max}$.
$1/e$ width $= \sigma\sqrt{2} = 1.41\,\sigma$ at $y = y_{max}/e$.

4. The Poisson distribution

The Poisson distribution describes all random processes whose probability of occurrence is small and constant. The probability for the event to occur x times in m trials is:

$$P_x = (m^x/x!)e^{-m}.$$

With Stirling's approximation

$$x! = \sqrt{2\pi x}\,x^x e^{-x}(1 + \tfrac{1}{12}x + \ldots),$$

P_x becomes

$$P_x \cong (1\sqrt{2\pi x})(m/x)^x e^{(x-m)}.$$

5. Miscellaneous relations

No. electrons/cm^3 air (NTP) $\cong 3.9 \times 10^{20}$.
1 cm^3 (NTP) of H_2/hr, if completely ionized, will produce 1.179 mA of H^+.
Density of air (NTP) $= 1.293$ mg/cm^3.
Decay rate of a level: $\tau^{-1} = \lambda$ (sec^{-1}) $= 1.52 \times 10^{15}\Gamma$ (eV).
Black-body radiation: $S = \sigma T^4$, $\sigma = 5.670 \times 10^{-8}$ W m^{-2} deg^{-4}.